MAN, CATTLE and VELD

Johann Zietsman

1st Edition

For More Information:

http://mancattleveld.com

http://profitableranching.com

Email: graybull@beefpower.com

INTRODUCTION (MCV)

PART I: MAN

PART II: CATTLE

PART III: VELD

APPENDIX

GLOSSARY

CONVERSION TABLES

INTRODUCTION (MCV)

I am one of those fortunate individuals who knew early in life exactly what they wanted to do. I felt predestined to finding practical solutions to improving the veld and breeding veld productive cattle that, with minimum assistance from man, could efficiently convert veld into quality beef. Little did I know it would be a long journey of learning and making mistakes before I understood enough about man, cattle and veld in order to make the relationship symbiotic.

My ideas and the many questions I had were moulded at an early age in accordance with my background. Being raised in a family where my father and his two brothers were running over ten thousand head of cattle on tropical sourveld in Zimbabwe meant lengthy discussions concerning such issues as breeds, veld management and nutrition. This was at a time when the scale was not in use, supplementary feed not commercially available and weekly dipping in plunge dips compulsory by law. The result was that I developed an insatiable appetite for knowledge leading to the reading of all farming magazines available in southern Africa and filing all relevant articles. Much general knowledge was gained including information relating to the work done by Prof. Jan Bonsma in the field of cattle breeding as well as efforts to improve the veld through Non-Selective Grazing by John Acocks and Short Duration Grazing by Allan Savory.

PHOTO 1: *A photo of the mid-1950s showing a herd of weaned calves bred by my father on tropical sourveld. No commercial protein supplements or drenching for internal parasites, but kept tick-free by plunge dipping. Are the "scientifically selected" cattle of today more productive on veld?*

The principles espoused by Bonsma on the one hand and Acocks and Savory on the other, although making sense to me, were generally deemed irreconcilable. In his heart Bonsma was a stockman and could not bear the thought of forcing cattle to graze non-selectively. Savory and Acocks were ecologists committed to rehabilitating and improving the veld. Their primary concern was using livestock as tools to improve the land. These opposing viewpoints were to retard progress. Nevertheless, I knew there must be a solution and decided to learn more by enrolling for a degree in Animal Science under Prof. Bonsma at the University of Pretoria, South Africa. This was the start to a journey of acquiring sufficient knowledge to bridge the gap between man, cattle and veld.

Whilst studying under Bonsma two issues came up that played a deciding role in how my career was to develop. The first was the assertion by Bonsma that "the Lasater Beefmaster herd was the most functionally efficient in the world". This was no ordinary compliment coming from a man who was world renowned for popularising the concept of judging hormonal balance by looking at an animal's morphology in addition to developing the Bonsmara breed on the basis of functional efficiency. The second issue was my turning down an invitation by Prof. Bonsma to join his staff in the Department of Animal Science. Although this could have paved the way for a potentially successful academic career my heart told me: No. I opted to get cow dung on my feet. Maybe this was the result of spending so much time during school holidays working cattle with my father.

It is interesting to consider how Lasater and Bonsma reached a similar end-point from very different starting points. Bonsma had in his mind's eye an image of a functionally efficient animal and bred and selected towards that by relying to a large degree on visual appraisal. Lasater, on the other hand, said he couldn't care what an animal **looks** like. He knew what a good animal should **be** like and selected accordingly. I came to understand that Lasater's approach, relying on nature to do the selection, is infallible. Bonsma's approach has two problems. Firstly, there are no other Jan Bonsma's in the world, although some pretend to be. Secondly, much of what you see in an animal is open to many interpretations influenced by fashion and personal agendas.

Although I was greatly influenced by Bonsma's thinking, particularly in regard to the influence of hormones on morphology and performance, I became aware that there were some serious flaws in his approach to breeding. My first inkling came when I witnessed an extremely well muscled young Bonsmara bull being culled at the Irene Bull Testing Station solely on account of a small white spot on its forehead. Another flaw, I believe, was his opposition to "pony-type" bulls – physiologically and sexually early maturing, small framed, well muscled bulls. This was an over reaction to the dumpy, over-fat bulls and cows of the mid 1900s resulting from selection for small frame and overfeeding by stud breeders in response to the requirement of show judges. Bonsma was influential in initiating the "frame-scoring" era of the 1970s and 1980s.

Fat became a dirty word and "lean and efficient", slab-sided bulls were winning show prizes and performance classes everywhere. Concurrent with this there arose the need to select for larger scrotums in an effort to counter the hormonal imbalance resulting from high frame scores. Although Bonsma must have been aware of the problem I do not think he fully appreciated where his opposition to a "pony-type" bull and preference for leanness would take us – poor veld adaptation and poor cow fertility. No degree of desirable sex hormones in a cow can compensate for poor body condition in determining fertility on veld.

I am convinced that this legacy of unwarranted sensitivity to colour, shape and type has had, and is still having, a detrimental effect on the productivity of the Bonsmara breed. The obsession with colour, I believe, excluded the Nguni in the composition of the Bonsmara. Had this been done the resulting Bonsmara would be far more productive today, particularly in respect of veld adaptation and fertility. Another factor undermining fertility is the fact that the so-called "pony" bulls are culled on the basis of selection for absolute growth and visual appraisal by breed inspectors. The result is a reluctance, or inability, of breeders to breed cows capable of producing their second calf at three years of age under veld conditions.

I am in no way suggesting that all Bonsmaras are poor animals. On the contrary, as in any breed, there are some extremely productive, or potentially productive, animals that are not being recognised as such due to erroneous breeding and selection practices. It is very disappointing that such a situation exists in the Bonsmara breed.

In contrast to Bonsma, Lasater selected for six economically essential characteristics and allowed nature to determine the colour, shape and type of his cattle. As an example, in selecting for fertility it became obligatory from 1947 for every cow in his herd to calve annually from the age of two years. It didn't matter what colour or shape the cow was. In addition, bulls were used in multi-sire herds. The most capable sired the most calves, thus increasing the genes for fertility in the herd. A bull's pedigree or colour was of no concern. The result, as described by Jan Bonsma, is that the Lasater Beefmaster herd is "the most functionally efficient in the world".

PHOTO 2: *With Mr. Tom Lasater in a herd of Lasater Beefmasters. Prof. Jan Bonsma labelled the Lasater herd "as the most functionally efficient in the world". This herd has been selected since the 1930s for six traits – fertility, hardiness, disposition, weight, milk and conformation. What has made this herd really stand out was the emphasis on fertility (calving annually from the age of two years). This was the common denominator upon which all other traits were built resulting in balanced cattle adapted to a particular environment.*

This does not mean that all so-called Beefmasters are productive animals. One only has to look at the situation in southern Africa to realise this is not so. Very few of these "Beefmasters" epitomise the Lasater philosophy. Although there aren't many Lasaters breeding cattle everyone has the potential to become one by following a simple and effective philosophy.

I consider Jan Bonsma and Tom Lasater to be the greatest cattlemen of our time. They certainly had a profound influence on my thinking. It is a travesty that so many protagonists of the breeds they developed only pay lip service to their philosophies. This is typical of mankind. We use their names, but conveniently ignore what they said or stood for.

After graduation and a three year involvement in research at Grasslands and Henderson Research Stations I returned to the family ranch in 1975 as manager. In between compulsory military commitments, as an Officer in the Rhodesian Territorial Army, I got down to ranching. Later in the year I was assisted by my father in purchasing my own property. This was the start to a real education in ranching.

In retrospect I realise that the freedom I had in making decisions, and mistakes, gave me an advantage over my colleagues involved in formal research. I learnt from the mistakes I made. I also developed a different perspective in that I could see the problems on the ground as well as the **many** opportunities. The realisation hit me, and was reinforced over time, that conventional ranching practices in the main are neither economically nor ecologically sustainable. Many times I have said jokingly: If we do the opposite of what is conventionally advised we would be right at least 90% of the time. I now realise that there is more truth than humour in that statement. If things are not going according to expectation you are probably going in the wrong direction which means you need to do an about-turn. Small degrees of change do not solve fundamental problems.

I also learned that the "impossible" can be done. Such as: the "impossibility" of inseminating 800 ranch cows; the "impossibility" of breeding yearling heifers to calve as two – year – olds; the "impossibility" of rearing decent calves born in January (mid rainy season) in a high rainfall tropical environment; the "impossibility" of achieving the highest average bull price in the country (equivalent of US $4000.00) for a 16 year period with so-called crossbred bulls.

In late 1976 my first Beefmaster crossbred calves were born. They were the result of using Lasater Beefmaster semen on Afrikaner-type cows developed by my father. This, incidentally, was the largest consignment of Lasater Beefmaster semen to leave the USA up to that date. In addition to these calves there were others resulting from the use of BBU Beefmaster and Santa Gertrudis semen from bulls with extremely high feedlot growth rate. The results were a revelation. Although the BBU and Santa Gertrudis calves weaned heavy they fell apart when fending for themselves on veld. This was particularly true of first-calvers who could not maintain body condition after calving. None of these calves or their progeny stayed long in the herd. This was a very hard lesson, particularly considering the fact that I was warned against the use of such bulls by my father as well as successful cattleman and neighbour, Harold Hilton-Barber.

PHOTO 3: *A magnificent Lasater Beefmaster sire, similar to the ones used in building the Bar Z Beefmaster herd. Although the resulting progeny were much more veld productive than those sired by imported Santa Gertrudis and BBU Beefmaster semen they did lack overall environmental adaptation, particularly nutritional adaptation. However, these animals were a good foundation for breeding the Veldmaster by infusing African breed blood in the form of the Mashona, Angoni and Boran.*

In contrast, the Lasater calves developed into magnificent animals manifesting all the economic traits featured in their selection programme. Amongst these were good temperament, tight sheaths and good muscling in bulls, milk and early sexual maturity. What they lacked was tropical adaptation in general and nutritional adaptation in particular – a characteristic I became aware of then and fully appreciated later.

I realised very quickly that in order for the Beefmaster to stand a chance to become adapted to the poor nutritional conditions of the high rainfall Zimbabwe Highveld, I would have to follow breeding and management practices very different to other breeders in southern Africa. Instead of the continual use of imported semen and striving to increase the proportion of popular bloodlines I decided to use my own bulls bred from cows that produced their **second** calf by the age of three. In order to concentrate these genes for fertility/adaptation, I used A.I. (Artificial Insemination) extensively – exclusively for 7 years and predominantly for a further 20 years.

A.I. became very effective through the synchronisation of oestrous. By restricting calving to a 42 day period, optimum in respect of nutrition, in excess of 80% of suckling cows cycled before the start of the breeding season. Synchronisation allowed A.I. to occur over an 11 day period at the beginning of the breeding season and an additional 3 – 4 days during the following oestrous cycle. The result was 80 – 90% of calves sired via semen and 55 – 60% of calves born within two weeks of initiation of calving.

This intensity of selection for fertility/adaptation led to much progress. A relatively large proportion of cows were producing their second calf at the age of three. Some cows weaned calves that weighed three-quarters their own weight. One of the outstanding features of Bar Z Beefmasters was the sexual dimorphism between bulls and cows. This is explained by the extreme effects between sexes, as seen in size and muscling, due to high levels of the relevant sex hormones. Such effects are also apparent in the African breeds that have developed largely through natural selection. Other differentiating features in bulls were a very tight sheath, relatively fine bone, medium frame, masculinity and a high meat: bone ratio – the opposite of what other breeders desired.

PHOTO 4*: Cattle being plunge dipped on the family ranch in order to control ticks. Weekly and fortnightly (dry season) dipping was compulsory by law. The result of this strategy was the breeding of dip resistant ticks and not tick resistant cattle.*

No animals were dosed in an environment teeming with internal and external parasites. My opposition to the use of anthelmintics went further than the fact that they killed dung beetles. Dosing had never been practised on the family ranch. Although some cattle may have been affected adversely the majority did well. The bulls were always in good condition – an indication of thriftiness and the absence of stress from internal parasites. I was not interested in breeding cattle that required dosing.

The fact that I grew up in a situation where cattle were plunge dipped weekly blinded me to the fact that, as with internal parasites, cattle must have inherent mechanisms protecting them from ticks as well as the diseases they transmit. I was aware of some cattle that were never dipped yet never had ticks on them. These were animals that, as calves, nearly drowned on the first attempt to dip them. They were never dipped again and subsequently came to the dip every week, but with no ticks on them although at certain times of the year the regularly dipped cattle had a considerable number of ticks. I was also aware that our indigenous cattle were never dipped prior to the intervention of modern man. It was the O'Neill brothers of Chivhu, however, who were moving away from dipping who inspired me to change.

Starting in 1986 no calves were dipped until the yearling stage when animals were strategically treated for the brown ear tick during the wet season by hand spraying on the head and neck. No dipping occurred during the eight month dry season although, at times, there was a heavy tick burden – this maintained the pre immunity to tick-borne diseases acquired as calves. It was very interesting to note that where these diseases were previously prevalent they only developed when animals came under stress.

The early 1990's was a period of much introspection. My cattle were performing very well under commercial ranching conditions at the officially recommended stocking rate; bulls were selling at record prices and the country's economy was strengthening. But, the veld was visibly deteriorating. This was forcefully brought home to me one day whilst walking through the veld. I was struck by two adjacent grasses of the same unpalatable species that were dead. One was level to the ground; the other stood a metre high. One was killed by continuous overgrazing; the other died as a result of a lack of defoliation. What was it in my management that could result in such divergent treatment of the same grass species? Clearly, a conservative stocking rate as generally advocated was not having a desirable effect.

My mind was cast back to Allan Savory and his involvement in the Charter Trial of the 1970's. This was a comparison between an orthodox One-Herd-Four-Paddock system and a Short Duration Grazing system under Savory's guidance. Over a period of 7 years Savory was able to carry twice the number of cows without the veld deteriorating relative to the Control. It was clear that stocking rate, or the number of animals, was not responsible for veld deterioration. This finding contradicted conventional thinking that was based on the premise that stocking rate determines whether veld remains stable or deteriorates. Although individual animal performance dropped by approximately 10% at double stocking rate in the Short Duration Grazing system, the return on capital investment remained similar whilst the gross margin increased by 28%. The drop in individual animal performance, however, blinded everyone to the other important positives.

Thinking about these results, many questions entered my mind. Although there was no veld improvement at stock densities equivalent to 16 paddocks per herd, what would happen at 1000 paddocks per herd? Would the same increase in paddocks not have a positive effect on animal performance? What about cow genotype and fertility? These questions should have been asked and answered by the researchers. But, twenty years later there were no answers – only feeble excuses such as "this approach is not currently advocated by the Department of Agriculture because there is no long term data to support these contentions" (Farmer's Weekly: 19 July 2002, p. 6). I needed answers and realised I would have to find them myself.

Apart from appropriate grazing management I knew I had to change my cattle's genotype further in order to bring harmony between cattle and veld. Although the use of home-bred bulls had resulted in positive change I realised further drastic change was necessary and that this could only come about through the introduction of African breed blood. Nutritional adaptation and increased resistance to ticks and screw-worm was essential. As a prelude to any major changes, one-half of the cows in a Beefmaster herd were inseminated with Beefmaster semen from home-bred bulls and the other half with indigenous Mashona – a small frame breed adapted to the high rainfall leached granite soils of the Zimbabwe Highveld. None of the resulting calves were dipped, dosed or treated for any disease. Not a single Mashona cross calf developed any problem whereas half the relatively adapted Beefmaster calves contracted sweating sickness (high fever, sweating, loss of hair and usually death even when treated) as well as coccidiosis (diarrhoea), resulting in several deaths.

The Mashona-cross calves had visibly less ticks and showed no sign of screw-worm infestation – a major problem in the ears of cattle damaged by the brown ear tick. In addition, the Mashona blood proved to be superior to conditions of poor nutrition as indicated by better body condition and higher fertility. The introduction of African breed blood (Mashona, Angoni and Boran) and the subsequent development of the Veldmaster breed would prove essential in maximising profit/ha in conjunction with appropriate veld management.

PHOTO 5: *Calf born to a Mashona bull and a Beefmaster cow. This was the beginning of the Veldmaster.*

As far as improving veld was concerned I knew the answers lay in implementing principles advocated by Acocks and Savory. The general feeling in the early 1990s was that any form of intensive grazing (more than 8 paddocks per herd) had no advantage in terms of veld improvement and only resulted in poor animal performance. The most intensive systems researched consisted of 8 – 16 paddocks per herd. This is ridiculous when viewed in the context of the degree of Animal Impact required to prepare a seedbed for seedling establishment, laying down un-grazed plants, improving rainfall effectiveness and manipulating time in order to improve nutrition. No wonder research results were negative or inconclusive. I saw this as an indictment against our researchers and not Acocks and Savory. It was clear I was not going to get answers to my questions from the academics.

I knew a breakthrough was dependent on hundreds to thousands of paddocks per herd. How could this be done physically and within the limits of finance? The human mind can be extremely creative or it can be an obstacle to progress depending on our beliefs. Most of us know that dairy cows on planted pasture in far away places like New Zealand can be controlled by single wire electrified fences. The same could probably be done in Africa with dairy cows on irrigated pasture. But, ranch cows on the veld? Never!

There is a man in South Africa by the name of Rudi Radley who did not know what could not be done. I visited him near Senekal in 1993. Crossing the boundary onto his property clearly indicated something was different. The veld appeared healthy with the grass a darker green colour. Even from a distance plant density appeared greater. For the first time I witnessed a practical demonstration of how electric fences can be employed easily and cheaply to create a virtually unlimited number of paddocks. This proved a turning point in my ranching career. I could not wait to get started, but it took me another two years of planning and overcoming psychological barriers.

It is important for the reader to understand what a breakthrough this degree of control of animals was. Conventional grazing management amounting to a few animals in a paddock or a few paddocks per herd is akin to a hunter – gatherer situation. Putting a few animals in a paddock for a few days or a few weeks or months does not constitute management. Management is only possible when mouths and hoofs can be controlled in respect of physical impact on plants and soil as well as the degree of selective grazing in relation to the time on an area and the length of the grazing cycle. This sort of control is only possible with the use of electric fences and, to a lesser extent, herding.

The fact that many breakthroughs can be attributed to non academics poses serious questions about the effectiveness of our education and research institutes. They need to be closer to ground level in order to appreciate the problems and see the **opportunities**. If this is not done quickly they will be left behind and become irrelevant.

The 12th of January 1995 is a day I will remember clearly for the rest of my life. Ninety cows and their calves in a tightly bunched herd under total control is a sight I will never forget, but was only a preview of things to come. Eventually I would run up to 700 cattle in a herd at a stock density varying between 1000 and 5000 mature animals per hectare. Several barriers had been crossed. These were in respect of animal control on a ranch scale, herd size and stock density. We were ranching on a different plane. The largest operation I have seen, and been involved with, is that of Beefcor near Pretoria, South Africa who run a total of more than 40,000 calves annually in a backgrounding system on veld. This is unique and a world first.

PHOTO 6: *The 12th of January 1995 - initiation of UltraHigh Density Grazing on Pumula, Karoi, Zimbabwe. This proved to be the start of the implementation of the recommendations of Allan Savory of high Animal Impact and severe grazing on a ranch scale. The use of portable electric fences made constant stock densities varying between hundreds and thousands of cattle per hectare a reality.*

Within two weeks, in the driest year on record, I realised I had to double stocking rate owing to improved utilisation of sourveld. This was achieved by moving cattle from leased grazing. During the third year stocking rate was treble the officially recommended rate. By the time I had to vacate my property in 2002 it was possible to carry 1 LU (Livestock Unit)/ha. This equates to a quadrupling of cattle on the same land. Conception rate and weaning weight of conventionally bred cattle declined approximately 10% owing to poorer body condition resulting from non selective grazing.

From a conventional point of view this appears to be negative. But, this needs to be seen in perspective. These stocking rates on this type of veld, even with a conventionally large number of paddocks, would have resulted in wholesale death due to malnutrition. This did not happen and the potential drop in performance was minimised due to the large number of paddocks per herd (in excess of 1000). Another way of looking at it - more in line with conventional thinking – is that performance increased to beyond 200% calving rate and 500kg weaners.

Veld composition, colour and plant density improved beyond recognition. There was a population explosion of indigenous and introduced legumes. Severely capped and compacted soil became humus-rich. A visitor from the USA commented that he had never seen so much ground cover in the form of grass litter or so many earthworms anywhere in the seasonal rainfall tropics.

Notwithstanding the obviously positive visual and documented results from monitoring sites, there were a few critics. Some were constructive and questioning whilst others were openly hostile. In the latter category was a very vocal group of professors, doctors of philosophy and self-styled range scientists from the University of Natal, South Africa who had the opportunity, but never made the effort, to see firsthand for themselves. I understand that their egos are at stake. But, are they going to bury their heads in the sand and continue to bark up the wrong tree?

As I am writing I have mixed feelings. I am extremely grateful for a fulfilling life and look forward to overcoming the challenges ahead. I am happy to say that we now have practical answers to the breeding of veld productive cattle that can be managed to improve the veld beyond recognition and attain at least a doubling of profit on a sustainable basis. I am frustrated by the apathy and ignorance shown by institutes such as universities, breed societies and the South African Agricultural Research Council. It saddens me that I no longer own land or cattle in my country of birth due to the actions of politicians.

It saddens me even more that my children and grandchildren, who are fourth and fifth generation Zimbabweans, may never have the privilege to work and improve this land. I take solace in the following Jonathan Swift quote: "*Whoever can make two blades of grass, or two ears of corn, grow where only one grew before deserves more of mankind than all the politicians put together*".

PHOTO 7: *Our home for many challenging, but happy years.*

PHOTO 8: *Saluting all cattlemen worldwide.*

I hope the foregoing brings perspective to what will follow. It is my wish that what follows will provide solutions to all who are privileged to be custodians of veld and cattle. May there be harmony between man, cattle and veld.

PART I: MAN

Man is the key to the issue of harmony between cattle and veld. Since the domestication of cattle, man has decided what is desirable or undesirable in terms of breeding and management. The decisions made in this regard are flawed by many factors unique to the human mind. It is said man is driven by perception rather than reality. In most instances our perceptions are based on prejudice, ego, fashion, arrogance and ignorance. But, a lie doesn't become a truth because everyone believes it neither does the truth become a lie because no one believes it. What is extremely important, and often frustrating, is opening minds to the truth because without a change of mind **nothing** will change.

This focus on man is an attempt at opening minds. I am no psychologist so my approach to opening minds, which on occasions has been described as confrontational, may not work for some. According to my assessment there are three categories of people. The majority are not committed to a particular point of view and can change their minds over time. A small group are actively looking for answers and will change when presented with the truth. The third group will fight tooth and nail to prevent change – even against their better judgement. This group is composed of people with vested interests. Foremost among them are the top stud breeders, show judges, breed inspectors, research scientists and other academics. I know I offend them. This is not intentional, therefore I make no apology. I have a message for everyone involved with cattle and veld and cannot get it across by beating about the bush. So, I am going to say it as I see it.

1. MAN: THE PROBLEM OR THE SOLUTION?

GOALS

If you have no specific destination in mind you can take any road and you will get there. On the other hand, if you have an inappropriate destination in mind you will end up being disappointed, whatever road you take. Does this not describe the situation as it pertains to cattle producers, researchers, advisers and academics?

The predominant goal of cattlemen, apart from the obviously flawed, relates to production per animal – calving rate, weaning weight, carcase grade, carcase weight, etc. This is achieved by selecting for performance in terms of absolute measures of growth rate, milk production and feedlot performance and then providing an artificial environment for animals to attain their genetic potential. Such an environment is provided through selective grazing at low stocking rate, burning moribund grass, energy feed and in many cases crop residue. Some of the more "advanced" studs provide improved nutrition in the form of irrigated pasture together with early weaning of calves onto calf meal to ensure reconception. In virtually all herds total chemical control of ticks and internal parasites occurs.

PHOTO 1.1*: If the goal is maximum production per animal it is impossible to fully utilise and improve veld. Management has to allow selective grazing at conservative stocking rates and increase production through external inputs. In terms of breeding, selection focuses on absolute performance parameters such as weaning weight and size.*

The scenario described above can only lead to discord between man, cattle and veld. Veld will deteriorate, cattle will need an improved environment in order to produce and man will be penalised with a low return on investment. But, as long as production per animal is maximised and the breeder rewarded for this by winning show prizes, special performance prizes and Cattleman of the Year competitions everyone appears to be happy. This is borne out by a proud winner of the *Zimbabwe Cattleman of the Year* competition, on the strength of his heavy weaners and high calving rate, who admitted that the carrying capacity of his veld had dropped to half of what it was 25 years previously.

PHOTO 1.2: *A goal of maximum sustainable profit per hectare requires an efficient functioning ecosystem and efficient grass conversion. Appropriate selection will result in the breeding of efficient grass convertors and appropriate management will result in maximum veld production and efficient grass utilisation.*

The first, and most important, step in achieving harmony is an appropriate goal. For such a goal to be universally applicable it must be concise and address economic and ecologic issues. A goal of **maximum sustainable profit/ha** fits this definition. The social issues involved in the running of a successful business are extremely important and need to be addressed – as important as the issues of appropriate management and breeding practices. However, they are not part of the goal but relate to the achievement of the goal.

Such a clear, simple goal expedites management and breeding decisions and concentrates the attention and efforts of everyone on a focal point. Time and effort should be spent on attaining the goal and not on formulating it.

I believe the results of the Charter Trials, referred to in the INTRODUCTION, would have had a different outcome had Allan Savory categorically stated that the issue was one of sustainable profit/ha within the context of a whole comprising veld, cattle and the predatory effect. There is no doubt about the fact that he achieved a greater profit/ha without deterioration of the veld. That this was achieved with conventionally bred cattle and a few paddocks/herd (8 – 16) should have given greater credence to his ideas.

Had Savory focused on a simple, concise goal and whole we would have been able to achieve harmony between man, cattle and veld much earlier. His contention that "all grazing systems fail", in reference to the many "failures" of Short Duration grazing, is founded on misconceptions and is unfortunate in that it retarded progress on the ground and created confusion and alienation. The stumbling blocks of insufficient stock density and nutritionally unadapted cattle – not the lack of a "holistic" goal – should have been identified and attended to earlier.

I was once asked how it was possible for me to be so successful in improving veld without a formally written "holistic" goal (pasted to the refrigerator door) describing in detail what the land and cattle should look like in the future. My reply was that I have a goal of **maximum sustainable profit/ha** and understand that the attainment of such a goal, within the grass-grazer-predator whole, is dependent on the functioning of **six** ecological processes, including micro-succession (genotype) which was not accepted by Savory as such. I concentrate on implementing breeding and management practices that enhance the functioning of these processes. Success is dependent on a clear, concise goal as well as essential knowledge required for managing the ecosystem effectively. The land and cattle will eventually reflect this.

A specific goal is essential. Without it all issues relating to management and breeding become a matter of opinion. The reader is asked to judge all critique and suggested practices in the light of a goal of **maximum sustainable profit/ha**.

THE HUMAN MIND IS AN ENIGMA

The human mind can be either creative or an obstacle to progress. Creativity comes from independent thinking. All organisations and institutes are intolerant of or, at best, stifle independent thinking. As an example, consider a conventional cattle breed society. What chance does a newcomer have of changing the *status quo* when the established breeders are **dependent** on the *status quo*? Another example is the fact that major advances in cattle breeding and management have come from people working at ground level and not at universities or agricultural institutes.

PHOTO 1.3: The human mind is truly an enigma. Photographed is a group of 18- month-old pregnant heifers that have been culled and ready for slaughter. According to this ranch's policy they should only have been bred at 27 months in order to calve at 3 years of age. The correct policy, however, would be to earmark them for inclusion into a nucleus herd to breed bulls for herd improvement.

How can we differentiate between fact and fiction? Do not be intimidated by academic bull. Just because a professor said it or it is written in a book does not make it factual. Question everything. Consider other points of view, particularly if they appear to be ridiculous. In the words of Albert Einstein: *"If an idea, at first, is not absurd there is no hope for it"*.

PERCEPTION AND REALITY

The world is driven by perception, whether real or not. Once a perception has become general knowledge it is very difficult to change it. Tom Lasater, founder of the Beefmaster breed, once said: *"I would rather make a rancher out of a boy off the streets of New York than one raised on a conventional ranch."* Such a person has no preconceived ideas when it comes to ranching. Some current misconceptions are:

VELD DEGRADATION IS THE RESULT OF TOO MANY ANIMALS

The major precept of conventional veld management is adherence to a conservative stocking rate resulting from the belief that degradation is the result of too many animals. Nothing could be further from the truth. More animals are generally needed to improve the land. They only need to be managed differently (See Chapter 17: "SOUTH AFRICA IS OVERGRAZED AND UNDERSTOCKED" - JOHN ACOCKS).

FERTILITY IS 10% BREEDING AND 90% FEEDING

Fertility is very highly heritable. In fact, there can be no lowly heritable survival trait. It all depends on the criteria being used (See Chapter 6: MEANWHILE, BACK AT THE RANCH............).

CROSSBRED BULLS DO NOT BREED TRUE

How can the use of crossbred cows be good and not the use of crossbred bulls? Both productivity and selection progress are greater when using crossbred bulls. (See Chapter 6; MEANWHILE, BACK AT THE RANCH............).

PEDIGREE RECORDING IS ESSENTIAL FOR BREED IMPROVEMENT

All animals have pedigrees, whether recorded or not. In most cases pedigree recording is a fruitless exercise. Performance pedigrees **may** be of value for **some** traits **if** accurate EBVs can be calculated. Generally speaking the concept of "purebred pedigree" is ridiculous and a big obstacle to progress.

BLUP TECHNOLOGY "WILL ALLOW EBVs OF DIFFERENT BEEF CATTLE BREEDS TO BE DIRECTLY COMPARABLE NATIONALLY AND INTERNATIONALLY"

This is a complete fallacy for the simple reason that the most important trait required by cattle, namely fertility, is subject to genotype x environment interaction. The characteristics that make an animal adapted to a particular environment (inherently good body condition) are the same characteristics that make it unadapted (inherently poor body condition) to a different environment.

Body condition (nutritional adaptation) is the primary determinant of practical fertility. BLUP is totally inappropriate in such a situation. If BLUP was what it is made out to be why are there no accurate EPDs for cow fertility? (See Chapter 6: MEANWHILE, BACK AT THE RANCH............).

FAT IS BAD; LEAN IS GOOD

Since the 1960s cattle breeders and producers have been brainwashed with the idea that "fat is bad". This led to the breeding of late maturing genotypes (large frame and lean) and the use of the Continental breeds. This suited feedlots using cheap grain as well as breeders striving for fast absolute gain since less energy is required for gain consisting largely of lean meat and water. Has everyone forgotten that a cow needs to be in good body condition in order to calve young and regularly? (See Chapter 6: MEANWHILE, BACK AT THE RANCH............).

"2 X 5 BONSMARA CATTLE COULD CREATE EXCITEMENT IN THE CATTLE INDUSTRY"

This refers to "Bonsmaras that grow post weaning 2 kg per day or better and convert feed (high energy feedlot ration) at 5:1 or better (Bonsmara 2008, p. 34). This is a ridiculous objective in the context of veld productivity.

Have the present generation of Bonsmara breeders lost sight of the goal of the founding breeders? Is **practical** fertility not the most important trait required for veld productivity? Would the breeding of 2 + 3 cows (calving at 2 and 3 years of age on veld) not be a wiser and more appropriate objective?

A LOOSE SKIN INDICATES GROWTH POTENTIAL

Rather than indicating the potential for growth a loose skin indicates a lost opportunity for growth. (See Chapter 6: MEANWHILE, BACK AT THE RANCH............). Bulls with a high relative growth rate and tight skin – equivalent to a 5kg packet containing 8kg of sugar as opposed to a 10kg packet containing 9kg of sugar – are regarded as "pony-types" and culled. Are these not the bulls required to improve veld productivity (cow body condition and hormonal balance)?

CATTLE NEED TO BE BETTER MANAGED IN ORDER TO ATTAIN THEIR GENETIC POTENTIAL

This means keeping cattle parasite free, allowing them to graze selectively and feeding high levels of energy in order for animals to produce at maximum levels. Surely it would be more prudent to breed animals to be in tune with their environment in order to optimise production per animal and maximise profit/ha.

"IN ORDER FOR THE BEEF INDUSTRY TO COMPETE WITH THE PORK AND POULTRY INDUSTRIES MORE EMPHASIS SHOULD BE PLACED ON FEED EFFICIENCY" (PHASE C FCE)

The rationale for this approach is that "70% of all cattle slaughtered in South Africa are finished in feedlots" and that "approximately 55% of the total feed and non-feed costs of lean meat production are required to maintain the cow herd weaning an 80% calf crop" (Bonsmara 2008, p. 33). What is the goal: Veld productivity or feedlot productivity? Assuming the goal is biased in favour of feedlot productivity: How are ruminants (cattle) ever going to compete with monogastrics in converting grain to meat?

The human mind is indeed an enigma. Cattle have an unfair advantage over pigs and chickens in converting grass into quality meat and, if managed appropriately, in improving the land. This is what they have been created to do. It is crazy to believe they must compete with pigs and chickens in converting grain into meat – as crazy as believing pigs and chickens must compete with cattle in converting grass into meat.

HEIFERS MUST WEIGH AT LEAST 300Kg BEFORE BEING BRED

This is a reflection of breeders' obsession with size and absolute growth. Animals with smaller mature size mature sexually at much lower weights and younger ages (See Chapter 6: MEANWHILE, BACK AT THE RANCH............).

AVOID INBREEDING AT ALL COSTS

Inbreeding concentrates genes. Is it bad if those genes are desirable? Is inbreeding not common in nature? (See Chapter 6: MEANWHILE, BACK AT THE RANCH............).

NOT MORE THAN 25 COWS PER BULL

Many bulls can serve double this number. Some bulls can do much better. A bull by the name of Dunlop produced 90 calves within a period of 30 days.

CALVE BEFORE THE RAINS

The result of calving before the rains in seasonal rainfall environments is heavier weaners with a higher production cost and lower selling price per unit of weight. In addition to this, the breeding/calving season is longer, supplementary feeding less effective, reconception rates lower and 14/15 month heifer conception rate low relative to calving in the middle of the rains. (See Chapter 6: MEANWHILE, BACK AT THE RANCH............).

HEIFERS THAT CALVE YOUNG NEVER GROW OUT

This may be true of some cattle, particularly if they are in the wrong environment. However, if they calve regularly from an early age they have achieved the ultimate in terms of productivity. The problem is man made rules that prevent many cows achieving this.

BULLS THAT BREED WHEN YOUNG ARE STUNTED FOR THE REST OF THEIR LIVES

A young bull that serves cows to the extent that he becomes stunted is certainly worth having.

CATTLE MUST GRAZE VELD LIGHTLY AND UNIFORMLY

The view is often expressed that cattle must not graze grass plants below a certain height and that when they leave a paddock all plants must be grazed evenly. This is a utopian dream, where there is a diversity of plants, unless cattle can be bred or trained to graze non-selectively and leave 50% of each plant. What can be done is to graze heavily (100% utilisation) and uniformly (non-selectively). (See Chapter 17: "SOUTH AFRICA IS OVERGRAZED AND UNDERSTOCKED" - JOHN ACOCKS).

CONFORMATIONAL DIFFERENCES IN CATTLE RELATE TO THE HIGH-PRICED CUTS

There is no significant difference in the proportion of the different cuts in a carcase whether looking at a Jersey or a Limousin. Carcase differences relate to meat: bone ratio and fatness.

YOU CANNOT MULTI-SIRE BECAUSE YOU WON'T KNOW WHO THE SIRE OF A PARTICULAR CALF IS

Is there a difference in the quality of calves that are the result of multi-siring as opposed to using single sires? The question to be asked is whether there is a good reason to identify sires. If there is, they can be identified through DNA tests.

WHITE FAT IS GOOD; YELLOW FAT IS BAD

South African producers of veld fattened beef with yellow fat (produced by carotene in green grass) are discriminated against in favour of feedlot beef with white fat. Apart from the fact that yellow fat is healthier for humans (high in anti-cancer CLAs) it also denotes a potentially (depending on management) more sustainable production environment.

FEEDLOTS SEEK HEAVY WEANERS

This is one of the reasons given for producing heavy weaners by calving before the rains. The fact is that heavy weaners are penalised in terms of what buyers pay per unit of weight. Why produce weaners with a higher cost/kg and lower price/kg?

FERTILITY IS THE MOST IMPORTANT DETERMINANT OF RANCH PROFITABILITY

Stocking rate is the most important determinant of ranch profitability unless a 200% calving rate can be achieved and cows can wean 500kg calves (See: Chapter 6: MEANWHILE, BACK AT THE RANCH............).

CONSTRUCTIVE OR OBSTRUCTIVE

The human mind is like a parachute; it only functions when open. Depending on our state of mind, thoughts and actions will be constructive or obstructive. Many factors determine this.

PREJUDICE AND PRECONCEPTION

Man judges new concepts in the light of his perceptions. If an idea does not fit into his current frame of thinking it is summarily rejected. This is particularly true of revolutionary ideas such as the use of Non-Selective Grazing and high Animal Impact to improve veld and increase carrying capacity. This is contrary to the conventional precept of selective grazing and conservative stocking rate. Even when presented with the facts some prefer not to see. This is especially true of people with vested interests such as conventionally thinking professors.

How can we overcome prejudice and preconception? Our education system, particularly at the tertiary level, must encourage independent thinking. As individuals we must continually question everything we believe in and challenge conventional thinking.

PEER PRESSURE

It takes strong character and a clear goal to swim against the current. Independent thinking makes this possible.

FREEDOM TO MAKE MISTAKES

Without the freedom of making mistakes progress would not be possible. Experience comes from trial and error. Mistakes have a way of highlighting a wrong idea. A mistake is only negative if it is repeated continually.

I have been fortunate in having had the freedom of making many mistakes and learning from them. A good example is the use of American semen from bulls with very high feedlot gain, referred to in the INTRODUCTION. Their progeny, the equivalent of 9kg in a 10kg package, lacked nutritional adaptation (body condition) and drought tolerance resulting in extremely poor veld productivity. Had I not made such a "good" and expensive mistake early in my career my understanding of nutritional adaptation and the importance of relative growth, as opposed to absolute growth, would not be as complete.

Fathers should allow their sons greater freedom. The experience they have comes from trial and error. The psychological barriers they have are due to a lack of mistakes they made.

BETTER NOT TO KNOW WHAT YOU CAN'T DO THAN TO KNOW WHAT YOU CAN DO

It is much better not to know what you can't do than to know what you can do. Actions are limited by thoughts. If you believe something is not possible then it becomes "impossible". On the other hand, if you do not know that something is "impossible" then it is not only possible, but highly probable.

In my consulting work I see many examples of the principle of "not knowing what you can't do" being played out. Virtually without exception, professionals without a conventional ranching background, but with interest in sustainable ranching, make breeding and management decisions the average rancher wouldn't dare make.

KNOWING MORE ABOUT LESS UNTIL YOU KNOW EVERYTHING ABOUT NOTHING

Education, particularly at the tertiary level, is characterised by specialisation. At graduate level, livestock students start specialising in animal science or pasture science with very little overlapping. Further on at post graduate level specialisation becomes even more intense with animal science students concentrating on genetics, nutrition or physiology. The end result is that more and more is learnt about less and less until the student knows a lot about very little. Professional academics eventually know everything about nothing and nothing about the greater whole – the grass-grazer-predator relationship – which is the minimum ranchers can work with. It is better to know less about more than more about less.

AN INNATE ABILITY TO COMPLICATE MATTERS

Man seems to think that if an idea or practice is simple it can't work. He spends time, effort and money on complicating matters. Consider "modern" cattle breeding. "Experts" try and do a balancing act with BLUP-derived EPD figures, of generally low accuracy, for antagonistic criteria in order to breed "curve-benders" that are raised under artificial conditions in an effort to improve veld productivity. Einstein described this flaw in man's thinking when he said: *"The problem with mankind is perfection of means and confusion of goals"*. If the goal in cattle breeding is simple and clear so will breeding and management practices be simple and clear (See Chapter 7: THE MOST PROFITABLE BEEF ANIMAL).

VESTED INTERESTS

This is probably the biggest obstacle to change and progress. Once you have nailed your colours to the mast it is extremely difficult to change those colours even if you know they are the wrong colours. Pride and ego are very strong emotions. I do sympathise with people finding themselves in this trap but, for their own sake, they need to admit being wrong, change and move forward.

This is a message to stud breeders, animal scientists and pasture scientists. You can't hold onto something that is false. Circumstances have led you to where you are. If you have made a mistake, accept it as part of a learning process and move on. No-one has a right to judge you since it is human to err. One mistake you cannot afford to make, however, is to arrogantly defend a lie.

INSTITUTIONAL IGNORANCE AND ARROGANCE

It is a serious problem when erroneous concepts become "institutionalised" and defended by arrogance. When this occurs at the level of universities and other institutes the ramifications are highly negative and far-reaching. Once a perception becomes entrenched in society it is virtually impossible to change it.

Do those arrogant professors who summarily reject a concept originating outside their sphere of influence, and not conforming to their ideas, realise what a disservice they are doing society? Universities and other institutes have a moral obligation to seek and disseminate truths instead of defending lies.

NO-ONE HAS A MONOPOLY ON THE TRUTH

The truth is not waiting to be invented by someone. Neither is it the domain of ordinary professors, or even extraordinary professors, and doctors of philosophy. The truth is part of Creation. Anyone with sufficient humility and hunger for the truth will find it.

Numerous breakthroughs in our understanding of how natural systems function together with how this knowledge can be applied to agricultural systems come from ordinary, or maybe not so ordinary, people. This is a terrible indictment against the establishment.

RESEARCH STATIONS MUST BECOME MODEL RANCHES

Agricultural research can be classified into several categories:

-       Enhancing natural processes. This type of research is essential, but not enough of it is being carried out. A good example of the application of such research is rumen stimulating supplements that enhance rumen function and the utilisation of poor quality grass. Another example of good applied research is the establishment of legumes and certain trees to fix nitrogen and increase the cycling of nutrients in order to increase soil fertility and grazing quality.

-       Intervening in natural processes. This leads to quick fixes, but the price paid in the longer term is very high and unacceptable in terms of environmental damage and related problems. Examples are the use of fertiliser, chemical (poison) control of ticks and internal parasites in livestock as well as the poisoning of bush.

-       Interesting but irrelevant. It is no major revelation for researchers to tell us after 15 years of measurement that the humus content of soil under veld in good condition is higher than under moderate or poor veld. Such information is guaranteed to advance an academic career, but it is of no value whatsoever to the man on the ground intent on improving his veld. Should they not be researching ways of improving veld condition?

-       Absolutely useless. Research has been done that "proves" that Animal Impact does not result in improved seedling establishment, increased water infiltration or the knocking down of mature grass. The stock density applied varied between a cow per 10 hectares and a cow per 1 hectare. This is the same as concluding that sugar does not sweeten tea when the maximum amount of sugar applied is only a few grains per cup. Such information is as useless as that that obtained from studying the wearing of cows' teeth relative to age or the recommendation that grass should not be defoliated close to the ground as such grass takes longer to recover. The latter information may be of value one day when cattle have been taught to graze at an even height.

-    The goal of research should be to understand how natural systems function and how natural processes can be enhanced. This must be done with the understanding that nature only functions within the context of a whole (See Chapter 4: MAN AND NATURE). The knowledge acquired must be applied in a manner mimicking nature and creating a functioning whole. Research stations must become model ranches allowing farmers in a similar environment to duplicate management and breeding practices. The ultimate objective and achievement for researchers should be the attainment of model rancher status.

PROFESSORS MUST FIRST BECOME MODEL RANCHERS

How many of our professors have herded cattle, handled cattle and experienced first hand the challenges presented by fickle environments? How many agricultural scientists (each specialising in nutrition, pastures, physiology, economics or genetics) realise that their specialised knowledge has very limited application in a whole consisting of a myriad of non-linear interactions?

Consider just one example of this flaw in our education system. One scientist is an expert on the effect of hormones on fertility and is able to identify the bull with the most desirable hormonal balance. A colleague of his is able to identify the most "efficient" growing bull from a Phase C feedlot test (FCE). Between them they select the most "fertile" and "efficient" gaining bull. What will the practical fertility of this bull's female progeny be on veld with poor nutrition? A herdsman will tell you that the most important determinant of cow fertility is body condition.

The scientist improves body condition with expensive feed. The herdsman knows that there are individual cows with the genetic ability to maintain body condition, enabling them to calve annually without expensive feed. Who has the greatest knowledge: The scientist or the herdsman?

It is essential that prospective animal scientists do an apprenticeship course starting as herdsmen and advancing through applied research and on to eventual model rancher status. The best of these can then move on to become professors.

THE ARROGANCE OF HERD BOOKS AND BREED SOCIETIES

The following are excerpts from a South African Herd Book Newsletter published by Bonsmara 2008:

"The increasing availability and sale of unregistered bulls from all breeds is of concern".

*"The availability of software and other services that make performance data available to commercial farmers in order that they may also **evaluate bulls** exacerbates the problem".*

"These sellers of 'bosbulle' (roughly translated as bush bulls or village bulls) do not have the costs of recording, inspections, performance testing and other Society related costs. The animals do not conform to breed standards, but are sold as bulls from breed X or Y".

"The broader commercial market needs to be informed and educated about the value of registered and tested bulls and the risks involved in using 'bosbulle'".

The unashamed arrogance of the above statements is clear for any open minded person to see. If the SA Herd Book had their way commercial cattlemen would be forced to buy stud bulls bred under the "guidance of the Agricultural Research Council and protection of the Breed Societies". God forbid such a situation.

If anyone has any doubt about the inflated image these people have of themselves and their cattle consider the difference between the so-called "improved" and "unimproved" breeds as reported in veld tests. The following examples should suffice:

- Omatjenne Research Station, Namibia. In a veld test, over a 14 year period (1992 – 2005), the indigenous and "unimproved "Sanga (similar to the Nguni) outperformed the "scientifically improved" Bonsmara and exotic Simmental in terms of production per hectare. In a drought year (1999), the respective calving rates were 79%, 63% and 50%. Total weaner weight produced was 5565 kg, 4462 kg and 2864 kg respectively.

- Matopos Research Station, Zimbabwe. In a trial comparing productivity measured on a per hectare basis (1979 – 1986) the indigenous Mashona far outperformed all other breeds including the exotics (Sussex and Charolais). The closest rivals were the indigenous Tuli and Nkone in addition to the Brahman. Of all the southern African indigenous breeds the Afrikaner has been the most "improved" (mainly visual appraisal by breed "experts"). The average calving rate of the Mashona was 77% relative to 59% for the Afrikaner. Productivity at weaning (kg/Livestock Unit) was 184 and 120 respectively.

What the pompous individuals from the SA Herd Book and Breed Societies should explain to the "unenlightened" commercial producers is why the "unimproved" breeds excel in veld tests when compared to the "improved" breeds. Could it be that the results are biased in favour of the "unimproved" breeds due to the fact that the trials were conducted on veld and not under stud conditions? Maybe the commercial producer is not so stupid. Maybe he appreciates the difference between **"survival of the fittest"** and **"survival of the prettiest"**.

2. SUPERSTITION AND MYTH

A serious problem encountered in cattle breeding is the viewpoint that man is the ultimate judge of what is desirable. There is also the belief that somehow some are more proficient than others at doing this. Add egos and vested interests to the mix and you have a perfect recipe for superstitious beliefs and myths.

SHOWS, JUDGES AND BREED INSPECTORS

What positive connection is there between shows, judges and breed inspectors on the one hand and veld productivity on the other hand? Why are the "unimproved" breeds more productive than the "improved" breeds? Are stud breeders really serious about increasing the veld productivity of their cattle?

PHOTO 2.1*: Show judging is a farce. It epitomises man's inflated ego and disconnection with nature. Its legacy is an ever changing fashion show unrelated to reality. Its consequences, as seen here, are man-made freaks with no place in the real world.*

THE MEN IN BIG WHITE HATS AND HIGH-HEELED BOOTS

Judging of cattle in the show-ring and herd inspections have nothing to do with cattle. They have everything to do with fashion and man's ego. That could be dismissed as harmless fun if it were not for the fact that the consequences are so negative and far-reaching.

Visual appraisal does have a place, but when the focus is on the individual and his apparently supernatural ability to judge an animal in terms of productive efficiency the plot is lost. By attaching value to such a farcical and obviously flawed process Herd Books, Breed Societies and individuals are party to the perversion and subversion of true values. The men in big white hats and high-heeled boots (show judges), together with their apprentices, have made a mockery of cattle breeding.

THE IMPORTANT IS MADE IRRELEVANT; THE IRRELEVANT IS MADE IMPORTANT

Judging is, by virtue of its nature, concerned with the superficial. Due to the emphasis that Breed Societies place on appearance, without appreciating the limitations of visual appraisal, there is a total reversal of the value of traits relative to productivity. What is important has become irrelevant and what is irrelevant has become important. Rather than downgrading cows that do not calve at 2 + 3 years of age, breed inspectors will accept cows calving for the first time at 39 months, yet cull heifers not conforming to their image of the "ideal type". What logic is there in discriminating against a certain colour, colour marking (or lack thereof) or twist of the scrotum (when investigations have proved no relationship with fertility)? Worse still is the culling of the most veld productive cattle on the basis of absolute measures of growth (weaning weight, weight for age, average daily gain) (See Chapter 6: MEANWHILE, BACK AT THE RANCH............).

PHOTO 2.2: *The bull shown here depicts man's muddled thinking. As a sexually early maturing Afrikaner from a herd where a proportion of heifers calve at two years of age it is an exception in a breed with a hormonal imbalance. Rather than being identified as an individual capable of breed improvement it was downgraded by breed inspectors on the grounds of a twisted scrotum. This is clearly a case of making the important irrelevant and the irrelevant important.*

THE EVER-CHANGING "IDEAL TYPE"

Nothing discredits judges more than the ephemeral nature of the "ideal type" of animal they conjure in their minds. If these images only stayed in their minds it wouldn't be a problem. The tragedy is that these images materialise owing to the power judges and inspectors have over stud breeders who choose to follow fashion. In the 1950s the "ideal type" was an overfed dwarf. In an overreaction to this, the "ideal type" of the 1980s developed into a lanky slab-sided freak ("draadkar") whose progeny had difficulty fattening in the feedlot, not to mention on the veld. They now seem to prefer a "middle-of-the-road type", whatever that means.

The influence that these "wise men" have over breeders is also evident in breeds that are not involved in competitive showing, but are subjected to compulsory herd inspection. It is pathetic to see how superficial characteristics are over emphasised and the most important characteristic, practical fertility (inherent body condition in addition to hormonal balance), ignored. Some will argue that inspectors are capable of judging fertility by visually assessing an animal's hormonal balance. The fact that they overlook is that there is a big difference between academic fertility and practical fertility (See Chapter 6: MEANWHILE, BACK AT THE RANCH............).

STUDS, ARTIFICIAL ENVIRONMENTS AND ARTIFICIAL CATTLE

Stud breeders, with possibly a few exceptions, are living a lie. Can they honestly say that cattle that are bred and raised in an artificial environment (total parasite control, above average nutrition) and, at best, selected for high absolute production (milk, growth, feedlot efficiency) will improve the economic efficiency (profit/ha) of the commercial producer? Consider this fact. Cattle raised under a stud regime can be extremely "productive" **if** the environment allows it. The appropriate environment includes selective grazing, (low stocking rate), energy feed, crop residue (if unavailable then hay), calving well before the rains (less parasites and disease), a long breeding season (allowing better reconception rates), not more than 25 cows per bull and delayed bulling of heifers (require time to grow out to at least 300 kg). The problem is that this "productivity" is inversely related to economic efficiency since all the practices mentioned lower profit/ha.

STUD CATTLE OR VELD CATTLE?

PHOTO 2.3: *An artificial environment plus man-made laws equals artificial cattle. The motel-like building in the background is sleeping quarters for stud cattle. These cattle epitomise "survival of the prettiest" and, although considered to be an "improved type", will only survive in an artificial environment.*

There is a big difference between stud cattle and veld cattle. They have to perform under very different conditions and set of rules. Stud cattle have to contend with man-made laws in an artificial environment. Veld cattle have to produce in a natural environment under the jurisdiction of natural laws. For stud cattle it is "survival of the prettiest". For veld cattle it is "survival of the fittest".

BREEDERS AND TRADERS

A breeder of cattle can be defined as someone who, through wise breeding and management decisions, improves the productive efficiency of a herd of cattle in a given environment. There are very few that fit this definition. Most can be referred to as traders. They buy bulls from popular bloodlines or continually import semen from overseas in order to "improve" their herds. They are not concerned with breeding productive cattle. Their concern is breeding the "ideal type", whatever that may be at any particular time. They are not breeders. They could just as well run a supermarket.

TRIVIALISING THE IMPORTANCE OF GENOTYPE

Stan Parsons talks about "the futility of genetics" in his book entitled: *If You Want To Be A Cowboy Get A Job*. Although his comment is directed at the antics of show judges and stud breeders, it does hint at a deep seated scepticism of the value of genotype in the overall context of ranch profitability. Such scepticism, although understandable, is very unfortunate. The concept of genotype x environment interaction and the importance of genotype in this context cannot be over emphasised. In other words, there are specific genotypes that will far outperform other genotypes in a particular environment (See Chapter 6: MEANWHILE, BACK AT THE RANCH............).

3. POOR SCIENCE

An unfortunate part of our thought process is the making of unwise decisions by trying to be too clever. To quote Einstein again: Man is characterised by *"perfection of means and confusion of goals"*. This is particularly true when we are involved with natural processes.

Nature is both extremely complex and very simple. It is so complex in how it functions that we will never understand the detail fully. Yet, it functions very simply in terms of the whole. The challenge for us is to know what our role is, in terms of breeding and management, in enhancing natural processes. We also have to know the boundary over which we cannot step without creating discord.

A combination of over confidence, ignorance and arrogance has caused us to step over the line separating our role and nature's domain. This is manifested in scientifically poor decisions.

"MAN MUST MEASURE" – Jan Bonsma

It is true that man must measure. The problem lies in what is measured and how those measurements are interpreted. **We have erred by measuring inappropriate criteria accurately and appropriate criteria inaccurately.**

THE BIGGER THE BETTER

Although individuals are starting to question a goal of high individual animal production, this is currently still most breeders' goal. This is particularly true when it comes to selecting for absolute growth (age constant weight; average daily gain), milk production (weaning weight) and feed conversion (feedlot feed conversion efficiency) whether EPDs or Indices are used. There is no appropriate (genetically discerning) measurement of practical fertility, hence the ineffectiveness of selection. The result is an inverse relationship between production/animal and profit/ha.

PHOTO 3.1: *An A.I. bull selected at the height of the frame-scoring era with high absolute growth and extremely poor inherent body condition. Apart from many other defects, such a bull's female progeny will have poor practical fertility, even under good nutrition. Such cattle are man-made freaks with no place in the real world – lean and "efficient" but absolutely useless.*

ABSOLUTE GROWTH IS ABSOLUTE FOLLY

For absolute growth results in poor inherent body condition and poor veld conversion efficiency. That is why the "scientifically improved" breeds require better nutrition in order to be "productive". The overall result is a decrease in profit/ha (See Chapter 6: MEANWHILE, BACK AT THE RANCH............).

PHASE C FCE IS POOR SCIENCE AND POOR MATH

Feed conversion efficiency (FCE) measured as kilograms feed per kilogram gain is mathematically incorrect and scientifically flawed (See Chapter 6: MEANWHILE, BACK AT THE RANCH............). The result is poor veld productivity and no drought tolerance.

SCROTAL CIRCUMFERENCE USED AS AN ANTIDOTE FOR LATE SEXUAL MATURITY

Although there is a positive relationship between scrotal circumference and early puberty it is only related to the hormonal component of fertility. Currently it is generally used as an antidote in countering a hormonal imbalance resulting from selection for growth/frame size (See Chapter 6: MEANWHILE, BACK AT THE RANCH............).

BEEF COW OR DAIRY COW?

The quest for heavy weaners has led to the selection of cows with too much milk relative to the nutrition provided by the environment. The result is lower reconception rates due to poor body condition or uneconomically high levels of feeding in order to maintain fertility (body condition) at an acceptable level.

GOOD HORMONES AND POOR CONDITION RESULT IN ACADEMIC FERTILITY

A perfect hormonal balance in a heifer or cow cannot compensate for poor body condition in attaining high fertility. In such a case it is solely of academic value. What value is there, from a practical point of view, in emphasising hormonal balance whilst selecting against body condition? (See Chapter 6: MEANWHILE, BACK AT THE RANCH............).

PHOTO 3.2: *A cow with too much milk relative to naturally occurring nutrition has difficulty conceiving whilst lactating.*

WHAT A LOT OF BULL!

How is it possible for breeders of a "scientifically improved" breed professing to breed for veld productivity to sell "heifer bulls", "specialist growth bulls", "replacement bulls", "early maturing bulls" and "all-rounder bulls"? Something must be seriously wrong with their thinking, the measurements they take and how they are interpreted. A good, veld productive, breed (bull) should surely conform to a uniform standard.

PHOTO 3.3: *This A.I. bull was "scientifically selected" and identified for breed improvement based on its performance in a feedlot test. There is a great deal wrong with him and the measurements used to identify him. He is a poor grass convertor (9-in-10 package). His female progeny will show poor practical fertility. The slogan "Man Must Measure" loses its intended meaning when this is the result.*

BLUP: IS IT SCIENCE OR ACADEMIC WIZARDRY?

What value is a BLUP derived EPD, with an accuracy of less than 30%, for fertility (calving tempo) as seen in a "scientifically improved" breed's sale catalogue? Is it not confusing that a bull, with no progeny, has a calving tempo well above average (50 vs. 38.4) while its dam has extremely low practical fertility (ICP of 580 days over 6 calves; reproductive index of 74)? Is this what "Man Must Measure" means? BLUP is not what it is presented to be.

NO UNIVERSALLY SUPERIOR GENOTYPE

Each environment requires a certain genotype in order to maximise productivity. The more varied the environments the more varied the genotypes need to be. This fact disqualifies the use of BLUP derived EPDs in comparing animals from different environments for characteristics sensitive to genotype x environment interaction. This is particularly true of an important trait such as fertility which is largely determined by body condition. Good body condition in one environment is dependent on certain adaptive features which will result in poor body condition in a very different environment.

PHOTO 3.4: *An "improved" breed in the wrong environment. No degree of "scientific selection" using current BLUP derived EPDs can change this fact. Whatever genes that allow cattle to be productive in a temperate environment make them unproductive in this tropical environment. Cattle cannot be compared across environments for the economically important traits.*

ACCELERATED RETROGRESSION

Certain criteria being used by breeders result in poor veld adaptation and productivity. Accurate measurement of such criteria (Phase C growth and feed conversion efficiency are measured in a controlled environment and as such are not subject to major genotype x environment interaction) will result in accelerated retrogression. It is the same as increasing the speed of a car on the wrong road; you will end up at the wrong destination quicker.

JUGGLING ANTAGONISTIC CRITERIA

There are some breeders who realise that many of the selection criteria they use are antagonistic. An example is size, conventionally measured feed conversion efficiency, milk production and growth rate versus body condition and fertility. By juggling different EPD figures, often of doubtful accuracy, they attempt to breed animals with acceptable birth weights, fast post weaning growth and reasonable mature size – the so-called "curve-benders". There is nothing wrong with such an ideal. The problem is the human factor. What is reasonable or unreasonable; acceptable or unacceptable; too small or too big; too short or too tall; too little or too much? Man continues to waste time, effort and money in seeking the illusive "ideal type". This is not science.

TREATING A SYMPTOM IS EXPENSIVE AND ADDICTIVE

Modern management is characterised by treating symptoms and not the causes. We spend large amounts of money on dips and de-wormers instead of using parasite and disease resistant genotypes and selecting for parasite resistance. At the same time we breed poison resistant parasites and simplify the environment (killing dung beetles and other beneficial insects).

Treating a symptom may be necessary in the short term. For example, in sourveld environments it may be wise to burn moribund grass before addressing the cause – low stocking rate and low stock density. Tick infestations may have to be treated strategically whilst developing immunity and increasing genetic resistance.

Continuous treatment of a symptom is addictive and expensive. One merely exacerbates a problem.

PRODUCTION FEEDS, CENTRE PIVOTS AND CALF MEAL

Stud breeders who resort to such drastic measures in order to decrease calving age and increase reconception rates are treading on very dangerous ground. The cause of the problem is poor nutritional adaptation. This has to be addressed by selecting for good body condition. This is painful for breeders caught up in the politics of breed societies promoting "scientific selection" because size, absolute growth, milk production and feed conversion efficiency (as currently measured) are antagonistic to inherent body condition – the major determinant of practical fertility.

Trying to solve the problem by increasing nutrition to such high levels is expensive and aggravates the problem. If you are a stud breeder selling bulls you are wittingly passing on a genetic problem to the buyer. This is highly irresponsible and dishonest if the product you are selling carries a tag of **"veld productivity"** and is bought by a commercial producer relying on production from the veld.

DIPS AND DRENCHES

The problem of ticks and internal parasites is not going to be solved with poisons. Dipping and dosing make cattle more susceptible to parasites and dependent on the continued use of poison. In addition, beneficial organisms such as dung beetles and oxpeckers are killed whilst creating populations of chemical resistant parasites. The only lasting solution is dependent on the breeding of parasite resistant cattle and not poison resistant parasites.

DECREASING STOCKING RATE

Everywhere stocking rate is being decreased in response to degrading veld and in an effort to satisfy the higher nutritional requirements of cattle resulting from inappropriate selection. This process will continue until grazing management enables the ecosystem to function effectively and cattle are bred and managed in order to utilise the veld efficiently (See Chapter 17: "SOUTH AFRICA IS OVERGRAZED AND UNDERSTOCKED" - JOHN ACOCKS).

Another consequence of decreasing stocking rate that never seems to be appreciated is the decrease in profitability. An increase in individual animal production cannot compensate for a decrease in stocking rate (See Chapter 6: MEANWHILE, BACK AT THE RANCH............).

ERADICATING ENCROACHING BUSH AND WEEDS

Bush encroachment is the result of weak grasses, lack of browsing and, in some cases, insufficient hot fire. Eradicating trees and bushes is not addressing the main cause of the problem – grasses weakened through a combination of overgrazing, under utilisation and insufficient Animal Impact. When intervention is required to decrease bush it must be followed by an appropriate grazing strategy in order to address the cause of the problem. It must also be appreciated that trees and shrubs are essential in increasing soil fertility and consequently grass growth. This is particularly important for inherently infertile soil and areas of high rainfall.

BURNING MORIBUND GRASS

Having moribund and grey grass is not a healthy situation. It indicates a breakdown of the carbon cycle with carbon dioxide going into the air instead of carbon compounds returning to the soil to form humus. This is the result of too few grazers and insufficient Animal Impact to return carbon to the soil instead of being released into the air. If burning is necessary to improve grass palatability then it must be followed with the appropriate management (Non-Selective Grazing and high Animal Impact) as soon as possible afterwards in order to obviate the need for subsequent burning.

4. MAN AND NATURE

MAN VERSUS NATURE

Man's association with nature is not a happy one. There are several reasons for this. Man's attitude is one of dominance driven by greed, ignorance and arrogance. Rather than enhancing natural processes we try to eliminate them and replace them with those of our own making. In terms of cattle breeding "survival of the fittest" has given way to "survival of the prettiest". Grazing management is preferred with monoculture pastures. It is preferable to fatten cattle in feedlots using grain. Rather than breeding tick resistant cattle we breed dip resistant ticks. In all the mentioned cases "productivity" requires external inputs that are costly and ecologically unsustainable. Until man learns to mimic nature in agricultural systems there will be discord between man and nature.

PLUNDERING BIOLOGICAL CAPITAL

My *Zimbabwe Cattleman of the Year* friend, who admitted that his ranch's stocking rate had declined by half over a 25 year period, is a good example of how modern ranch "productivity" is achieved by the plundering of biological capital and **managers being rewarded for it**. The award was made, in part, on the very high individual performance of animals measured as weaning weight, calving rate and feedlot performance.

In order to attain the desired "productivity" a three-way crossbreeding system using a reasonably adapted breed, a British breed and a Continental Dual Purpose breed was followed. Separate herds of all three parent breeds were maintained under an above average nutritional regime in order to breed replacement bulls. Selection in all three herds emphasised growth. All herds, including the commercial herd, were kept parasite free by regular dipping and dosing. Veld management was implemented using a 1 Herd: 3 Paddock system with continual grazing and deferred seasonal rests. Selective grazing on a continual basis, except for the seasonal rests, together with high levels of feed supplement allowed all animals to perform at individually high levels. The conservative stocking rate was occasionally revised downwards due to bush encroachment and poorer individual animal performance

Any outsider can see that this sort of breeding and management, although highly commendable when judged in terms of individual animal performance, is totally unsustainable from an ecologic and economic (return on capital and profit/ha) point of view. **If** the goal of this rancher and reference point of the competition judges had been **maximum sustainable profit/ha** then this ranch would have been a good example of how things should not be done. Criticism should not be leveled at my friend. He was just following to the letter what the book was saying. If his breeding and management practices were presented as part of a thesis at university or college he would have passed with flying colours.

PHOTO 4.1: *The consequence of focussing on individual animal production and failing to see the bigger picture. Although this cow with an 8-month-old calf weighing 360 kg was "productive" due to external inputs and selective grazing at a low stocking rate the result was veld degradation. Under a regime of Non-Selective Grazing she was unable to conceive annually.*

POISON

Africa and parts of Asia are unique in regard to the fact that cattle, and other ruminants, evolved with many parasites and the associated diseases. The result is a high degree of genetic resistance to the parasites as well as the diseases they transmit. This degree of resistance is proportional to the severity of parasite infestation and disease virulence. In addition to some research data there is much anecdotal evidence indicating these genetic differences. For example, the N'Dama breed of cattle of West Africa is completely resistant to trypanosomiasis – a disease transmitted by the tsetse fly. From personal experience I know that both the Angoni and Mashona are highly resistant to sweating sickness. This is a disease situation caused by toxins that are transmitted to cattle via a tick, with calves being more susceptible than mature cattle. There are many such instances of genetic resistance. As a rule, the degree of genetic resistance is related to the severity of parasites and diseases where certain breeds and ecotypes developed.

The point is that there are genotypes available that require no, or only strategic, chemical control of parasites. Why is this not the preferred option? There are several reasons:

- The erroneous connection being made between production and profit. There is a cost involved in production above that provided by the environment, unless the input enhances a natural process. When using poisons there is the added cost of environmental degradation.

- The so-called "improved" breeds can not survive where they are at the mercy of endemic parasites and diseases.

- Changing to the so-called "unimproved" breeds is too drastic a step for most breeders. There are too many misconceptions that have to be cleared from their minds.

- There is a great deal of money to be made in producing and selling veterinary products such as antibiotics, dips and drenches.

FERTILISER

The compulsive use of fertiliser to attain maximum pasture "productivity" is not economically or ecologically sustainable, neither is it a requirement for **maximum sustainable profit/ha**. This can be achieved with appropriate grazing management of a pasture consisting of at least several species of locally adapted grasses, legumes and deep-rooted trees and shrubs. There may be a place for the application of deficient nutrients in the form of fertiliser and/or the application of lime to address soil pH, particularly in the initial stages. Pasture productivity and longevity is dependent on plant composition and grazing management.

SURVIVAL OF THE PRETTIEST

Nothing in cattle production depicts man's ignorance and arrogance, relative to nature, more than judges and breed inspectors deciding what is desirable or undesirable. In more modern times man is aided by mathematical models. The common denominator is man at his worst in terms of ignorance, arrogance, vested interests, prejudice and preconception. The result is "survival of the prettiest" where "pretty" is determined by what is currently in vogue.

NATURE IS BOTH COMPLEX AND SIMPLE

In the world around us there are two broad categories of success and failure. In the fields of mechanics and engineering great progress has been made. Look at transport and communications. Engineering is an exact science conforming to the laws of mathematics and physics. Interactions are linear and predictable. In the natural world man's testimonial is generally one of failure. This is due to the fact that in nature interactions are non-linear and unpredictable. We cannot manage natural systems from a mechanical perspective, as currently attempted.

In a narrow, mechanical sense, bull fertility is basically determined by hormonal balance. Such a bull could theoretically be identified by semen evaluation and a serving ability test. Assuming that such a bull will pass a desirable hormonal balance to his female progeny, will that mean that they will be highly fertile? That depends on the nutritional status of the cow herd and the inherent body condition passed on by the bull in question. Cow fertility is dependent on hormonal balance **and** body condition.

Body condition depends on environmental factors (feed supplement; time of calving relative to seasonal variation in nutrition) as well as genetic factors (milk production, frame size, climatic adaptation, parasite and disease resistance as well as individual appetite). Conventional management and breeding decisions are related to a very narrow goal of production/animal. This has a negative impact on body condition, requiring counter measures such as reduced stocking rate and higher feed levels. Such measures and counter measures are a feature of management concentrating on detail as opposed to seeing the greater picture.

We have a choice. We can make our relationship with nature extremely complicated or very simple. Trying to manage the detail will lead to frustration and failure because at this level nature is too complex. Understanding the greater picture and what our role is allows management and breeding practices to become very simple and rewarding.

ONE PLUS ONE IS NOT TWO

In nature, one plus one does not equal two. Water is a compound (whole) composed of hydrogen and oxygen. No amount of studying hydrogen and oxygen will tell you anything about water. Similarly, no amount of studying cattle and grass independently will tell you much, if anything, about the characteristics of a whole which is also composed of predators or the predatory effect.

The problem with studying nature from a reductionist perspective is that the conclusions drawn are not entirely valid in the context of a whole. The performance results of bulls measured in a feedlot test have little relevance to veld conditions and even less to a whole with the predatory effect (high density grazing). A bull with a fast growth rate and good feed conversion figures (conventionally measured) is unlikely to sire fertile females on sourveld (poor nutrition), even if he has well developed testicles and good secondary male characteristics. The reason for this is that feedlot performance (daily gain; feed conversion efficiency) is genetically antagonistic to maturity rate (inherent body condition). Inherent body condition (early physiological maturity) is the prime determinant of cow fertility on veld.

BETTER TO KNOW A LITTLE ABOUT A LOT THAN A LOT ABOUT A LITTLE

If the reductionist approach is inappropriate in analysing nature then we need to study the whole. In essence this means that it is better to know a little about a lot than a lot about a little. Rather than measuring feed conversion efficiency over a limited period in an animal's life (negatively correlated to inherent body condition) we should measure the end result of efficient grass conversion (maturity rate; body condition) at a particular age (See Chapter 9: SELECTING FOR PROFIT). Rather than measuring a bull's microscopic fertility in detail (semen analysis) we should measure the components of his practical fertility – breeding ability and physiological maturity rate (See Chapter 9: SELECTING FOR PROFIT).

PREDATORS ARE ESSENTIAL

Without the fear of predation, severe grazers such as buffalo, wildebeest or cattle will graze singly or in small groups. In the presence of predators such as lion and hyena they will bunch together in large herds. The effect on plants and soil are completely different. In the first instance selective grazing will occur (grazed and un-grazed grass) with both soil compaction and lack of soil disturbance (over trampling and no trampling). In the second instance there will be an even grazing of grasses and trampling of soil. In the first instance veld deteriorates; in the second instance veld improves.

In grazing management we have to create a functioning whole by simulating the presence of predators. This can be accomplished by using electrified fences or physical herding in order to control stock density and time. If this is done and, in terms of breeding, we accelerate natural selection the results will be unbelievable. From this perspective nature is very simple to understand. But, if we go the conventional route of trying to analyse and manage detail, nature becomes too complicated to understand and manage resulting in failure.

WORKING WITH NATURE

Why is it so difficult for man to work with nature – to mimic and enhance natural systems? I believe the reason is less to do with ignorance and much more to do with arrogance, particularly at the academic and institutional levels.

OBEYING NATURAL LAWS

We have two clear options. Either we accept the supremacy of nature and its laws and rest content with the resulting harmony **or** we follow the whims and arbitrary standards of man and prepare for the inevitable chaos. If we desire harmony and sustainable productivity we need to enhance natural processes and **accelerate** natural selection. It is as simple as that.

ENHANCING NATURAL PROCESSES

Examples of enhancing natural processes are increasing effective rainfall, aerating the soil, increasing the availability of nutrients to plants, increasing the flow of solar energy and improving plant composition. This can be done on veld by the appropriate management of the hoofs and mouths of severe grazers. The breeding of parasite and disease resistant cattle that do not require environmentally damaging chemicals for survival is another example. A very good example of the appropriate use of technology is rumen supplements (urea) and tannin neutralisers (polyethylene glycol) to increase grass and bush intake and utilisation. Imagine what progress can be made by spending money on mimicking nature rather than fighting it.

ACCELERATING NATURAL SELECTION

Survival of the fittest (most veld productive) and the rapid increase of these genes should be our mission in terms of livestock breeding. On an individual and herd basis this can be done easily – the knowledge is readily available. At the national and breed level the situation is different. Archaic concepts and laws must first be revoked. How are animal and pasture scientists going to be convinced that their thinking is wrong? Who is going to convince SA Studbook and its affiliated Breed Societies that their ideas and activities are out of sync with the natural world?

5. ACCORDING TO THE EVIDENCE

I believe that, as fully explained later, we now have the theoretical and practical knowledge for stockmen to **at least double profit/ha on a sustainable basis**. The evidence is contrary to popular belief but is there, on the ground, for those with an open mind to see. However, there are those who don't want to see regardless of the evidence. The vast majority of professors, lecturers, consultants, veterinarians and stud breeders fall in the latter category. The problem is that the average stockman will choose to believe them on the strength of their status. After all, many of them have the title of Prof. or Dr. before their name. In the mind of the average person they must be right. What do the facts tell us?

"IMPROVED VERSUS UNIMPROVED"

The evidence, at least in Africa (Omatjenne, Namibia and Matopos, Zimbabwe), is that the breeds least affected by "modern and scientific breeding methods" are the most productive on the veld (sustainable profit/ha). Why is this so? What justification is there for Phase C and D tests? Where is the logic in the accurate measurement (BLUP derived EPDs) of inappropriate criteria (FCE and absolute growth)? These questions are directed at the South African Stud Book Association and its affiliated Breed Societies as well as Professors of Animal Science.

DOUBLING OF STOCKING RATE

Since the early 1960s numerous individual stockman, following the recommendations of Acocks and Savory, have been able to double the stocking rate of their properties relative to conventional management. There are instances of a quadrupling of stocking rate. Details are provided in Part III of this book.

The Charter Estate Trial in Zimbabwe that was monitored for 7 years during the 1970s by researchers proved that it was possible to double stocking rate, relative to the conventional norm, without veld degradation. Why is the feeble response of pasture scientists (Farmer's Weekly, 19 July 2002, p. 6) that "there is no long-term data to support these contentions"? What have they been doing for the last 50 years? How many of them have tested the effect of time-controlled high Animal

Impact (hundreds to thousands of animals per hectare) on the ecosystem? These questions are directed, in particular, at the academics from the University of Natal in South Africa who have been the most vocal critics of time-controlled high Animal Impact and severe grazing.

EITHER ACCEPT OR IGNORE THE EVIDENCE

If the goal is maximum sustainable profit/ha then the evidence suggests that modern breeding and grazing management practices are retrogressive. This means that many, if not the majority, of principles adhered to and taught by the academics are wrong. Those who have built their reputation or business on these false premises such as the Agricultural Faculties at Universities, the Agriculture Research Council, Stud Book, Breed Societies and conventional stud breeders will ignore or try and counter the evidence. However, those who find themselves lower down the hierarchical ladder with their feet closer to the ground will start questioning conventional wisdom. Those furthest removed from agricultural academics will be in the best position to accept and embrace the obvious.

It is said that there are three levels at which evidence, contrary to convention, is debated. Initially, and particularly at the higher echelons of learning, it is ridiculed. With the passing of time a stage is reached where it is violently opposed. Eventually it is regarded as self evident and anyone not accepting it as a fool. Will a professor ever accept that he was a fool? I doubt it.

As far as the academics are concerned I believe most are currently at the "violently opposed" stage. They either fight or flee. There is no point in trying to engage them in meaningful debate. Let them be. In any case they are no longer relevant to the debate. Facts on the ground have overtaken them. Until professors start their careers as herdsmen and advance to model rancher status there is no hope for universities. In the same way that mind shifts in veld management and cattle breeding were made by people with their feet on the ground, change will only occur at ground level.

PART II: CATTLE

6. MEANWHILE, BACK AT THE RANCH............

Things are not always what they appear to be neither are they always what they are made out to be. There has always been a discrepancy between what the "experts" say and experience on the ground. Why are the "unimproved" breeds superior to the "improved" breeds in veld tests? Why do some ranchers experience a dramatic increase in veld productivity and stocking rate when applying time-controlled high Animal Impact when research indicates this is not possible? Why test bulls in a feedlot when their female progeny have to perform on the veld? Why produce 300kg weaners that require a higher production cost/kg and return a lower sale price/kg? Why breed cows to calve at a time when veld nutrition is at its worst?

CATTLE HAVE A DUAL ROLE

We have become so obsessed with high individual animal performance, measured in absolute terms that, we no longer appreciate where cattle fit into an ongoing process of creation. The primary role of cattle, and other hard hoofed grazers (as achieved by the predatory effect), is the enhancement of the natural processes in a grassland/savannah ecosystem. The secondary role, but highly important for man, is the efficient conversion of veld into a marketable product. Neither of these roles is being fulfilled.

Conventional grazing management is akin to a hunter-gatherer situation with, at best, some control of time (time in and out of a paddock) resulting in insidious veld deterioration. The breeding of cattle is focused on absolute measures of performance. Management is aimed at allowing animals to achieve their unnatural genetic potential. Veld conversion efficiency is poor and input costs, to allow animals to be "productive", very high.

It is essential to appreciate that cattle are an integral part of the ecosystem. They are subject to certain natural laws and they have to fulfill certain important functions. If there is harmony between man, cattle and veld then profit/ha can be doubled (at least) relative to the best conventional management. However, these laws and functions are being disregarded by man owing to ignorance and arrogance.

SCIENTIST LOGIC AND HERDSMAN LOGIC

People see things through different eyes depending on their background and experience. The average animal scientist relies largely on a theoretical background whereas the average herdsman draws conclusions from first hand experience on the ground. Is it possible that the herdsman is more scientific in his approach than the conventional scientist?

To an academic a masculine, hormonally balanced bull with a good scrotal circumference and good growth and feed conversion figures (Phase C Gold Merit bull) must produce fertile, productive heifers. In response to concerns from cattlemen that this might not be so he analyses the fertility of female progeny of Gold Merit and Sub-Merit bulls (those that scraped through the test and escaped being slaughtered) and comes to the conclusion that "breeders can use Gold Merit bulls with confidence, without fear of negative reproduction". This is in spite of the fact that the daughters of the top performing bulls had a 19 day longer inter calving period (ICP) between their first two calvings (Bonsmara 2007, p 34). This equates to a 5% difference in calving rate. To an academic, defending his theories, such a difference is considered to be insignificant.

To a cattleman, whose main concern is profit, such a difference is highly significant. What further escapes scientist logic is the fact that the daughters of the so-called top bulls are **definitely** not more fertile than those of the so-called inferior bulls. If one assumes that fertility is by far the most important trait required by cattle, what justification is there for classifying bulls in terms of "merit" that is indifferent, or contrary, to fertility?

The following scenario highlights the difference between scientist logic and herdsman logic. On the advice of an animal scientist a rancher, intent on improving the productivity of his herd, buys a Gold Merit bull. He is disappointed when the daughters of this bull have a low reconception rate despite their feminine appearance. The problem is judged to be poor body condition. The scientist advises him to improve nutrition by decreasing stocking rate, burning moribund grass and increasing energy feed. He is further encouraged to wean calves from first calvers onto calf meal at the age of two months in order to ensure a high reconception rate. He does as advised and judging by the increase in fertility the advice seems sound.

The herdsman responsible for the day-to-day management of the herd does not understand the logic behind these decisions. Why decrease cattle numbers and then burn excess grass? From experience he also knows there are cows in his herd that maintain body condition and calve annually without special attention. Would it not be better, he thought to himself, if they bred bulls from these cows instead of buying expensive bulls reared and tested under artificial conditions?

Who has the greatest wisdom: The scientist or the herdsman? There is a chasm between scientist logic and herdsman logic. They live in different worlds. One lives in an artificial, man-made world; the other lives in the real, natural world. One addresses symptoms; the other recognises causes. The only way this gap in thinking can be bridged is for scientists to get sufficient cow dung on their feet. Then the words of Thomas Huxley, eminent British scientist, will become true when he said: *"Science is nothing but organised common sense"*.

THE SMALLER AND HEAVIER THE BETTER

There is a relationship between size, growth rate, grass intake, maturity rate, body condition and efficiency of feed conversion that is essential to understand. Ignorance of this relationship has led to the breeding of cattle that require higher levels of nutrition in order to be "productive".

TABLE 6.1: THE AMOUNT OF ENERGY (MJ ME) REQUIRED BY DIFFERENT SIZE STEERS AT DIFFERENT GROWTH RATES IN ORDER TO GAIN A TOTAL OF 1 KG LIVEWEIGHT (Derived from the British Agricultural and Forestry Research Council, 1993)

ADG \ Kg	150	200	300	400	500
0.1	250	300	390	500	600
0.2	140	**165**	220	275	330
0.3	103	123	**160**	200	240
0.4	85	100	130	**160**	192
0.5	74	86	112	138	**164**
0.6	65	78	100	123	145
0.7	60	71	91	111	132
0.8	56	67	85	104	122
0.9	52	63	80	98	115
1.0	50	60	76	93	108

ADG = AVERAGE DAILY GAIN (KG)

TABLE 6.1*: THE AMOUNT OF ENERGY (MJ ME) REQUIRED BY DIFFERENT SIZE STEERS AT DIFFERENT GROWTH RATES IN ORDER TO GAIN A TOTAL OF 1KG LIVEWEIGHT (Derived from the British Agricultural and Forestry Research Council, 1993).*

The figures in Table 6.1 are derived from animal research work (British Agricultural and Forestry Research Council, 1993) and refer to the total energy (maintenance and growth) required by different size steers at varying growth rates to gain a total of 1kg of live weight. For example, a 200kg steer growing at a rate of 0.1kg/day uses 30 units of energy per day. Over a 10 day period a total of 300 units (10 x 30) of energy is consumed in order to gain a total of 1kg (10 x 0.1kg) live weight. However, at an ADG (average daily gain) of 1kg a total of 60 units are consumed resulting in more efficient growth (60 units vs. 300 units per kg gain). Each figure in the table represents the energy required for 1kg total gain. This enables animals of varying size and growth rate to be compared in terms of efficiency. Such comparisons result in the emergence of some extremely important principles.

THE FASTER AN INDIVIDUAL ANIMAL GROWS THE GREATER THE EFFICIENCY

Regardless of size, the faster an animal grows (the larger the intake) the greater the efficiency. A 400kg steer growing at a rate of 0.5kg/day requires a total of 138 (2 days x 69 units/day) units of energy to gain 1kg. At a growth rate of 1kg/day the requirement is 93 units – a large difference in favour of the faster growth rate. The reason for this difference in efficiency at different growth rates is the difference in total maintenance requirement to attain a gain of 1kg. The daily maintenance requirement of a 400kg steer is 45 units, regardless of growth rate. At a growth rate of 0.5kg/day a total of 138 units of energy are required of which 90 units (45 x 2 days) is solely for maintenance. The maintenance requirement at a growth rate of 1kg/day is 45 units out of a total of 93 units. This difference in total maintenance requirement, which is essential but unproductive, accounts for the difference in growth efficiency (relative to growth rate) on an individual basis.

SMALLER ANIMALS ARE MORE EFFICIENT AT THE SAME GROWTH RATE

When animals of varying size grow at the same rate, the smaller animals are more efficient. For example, a 200kg steer gaining 0.5kg/day is much more efficient than a 400kg steer also gaining 0.5kg/day (86 units vs. 138 units).

It is very clear that animals of varying size cannot be compared on the basis of absolute growth (ADG or weight). The variation in size has to be considered. This applies to the normal size variation that occurs in any herd.

EFFICIENCY IS THE SAME WHEN GROWTH IS PROPORTIONAL TO SIZE

Many examples in Figure 6.1 make this principle absolutely clear. A 200kg steer gaining 0.2kg/day, a 300kg steer gaining 0.3kg/day a 400kg steer gaining 0.4kg/day and a 500kg gaining 0.5kg/day are equally efficient (160 to 165 units/kg gain).

This principle, as well as the preceding one, invalidates all comparisons done on the basis of absolute growth rate (ADG) or time constant weight (weaning weight, yearling weight or 18 month weight). This means all current growth tests discriminate against the most efficient animals.

SMALLER FRAME ANIMALS HAVE AN UNFAIR ADVANTAGE

Why is it that the smaller frame animals in a herd or the smaller frame breeds are always in better body condition? Why do the smaller species of mammals (mice) have a faster maturity and reproductive rate than the larger mammals (elephant)? The answer lies in feed intake.

An animal's feed intake is influenced by many variables such as climatic adaptation, resistance to parasites/diseases and individual appetite. These characteristics are highly heritable and individualistic. One characteristic that influences intake regardless of the aforementioned ones is frame size. However, the relationship is not proportional to size but to metabolic size (Kg to the power of 0.75) which is a function that decreases, relative to size, the larger the animal. This means that the **absolute** intake of a larger animal is more than that of a smaller animal, but its **relative** intake (intake: size) is less. Conversely, the smaller animal consumes more in proportion to its size resulting in faster growth relative to size (more efficient feed conversion measured on a energy: energy basis) as well as better body condition and higher fertility (See Figure 6.1).

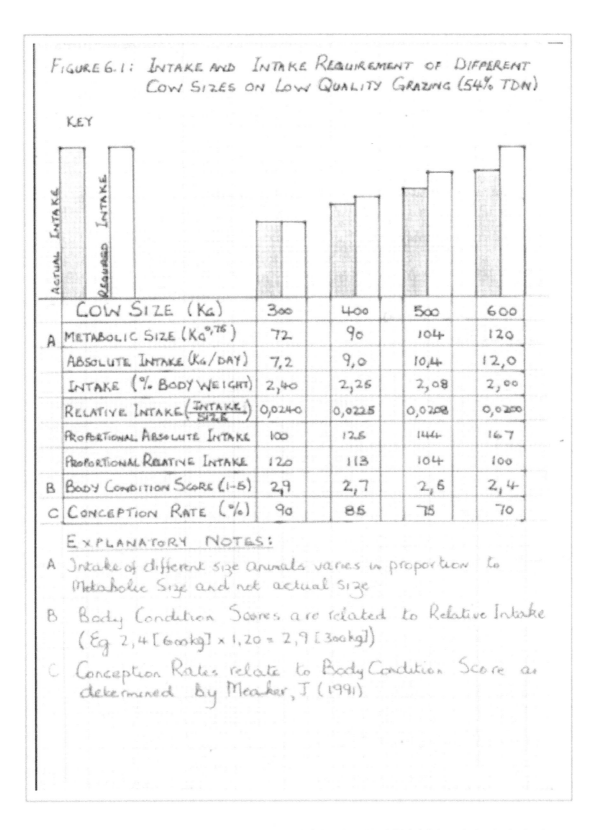

FIGURE 6.1: INTAKE AND INTAKE REQUIREMENT OF DIFFERENT COW SIZES ON LOW QUALITY GRAZING (54% TDN)

KEY

	COW SIZE (Kg)	300	400	500	600
A	METABOLIC SIZE (Kg$^{0.75}$)	72	90	104	120
	ABSOLUTE INTAKE (Kg/DAY)	7,2	9,0	10,4	12,0
	INTAKE (% BODY WEIGHT)	2,40	2,25	2,08	2,00
	RELATIVE INTAKE ($\frac{INTAKE}{SIZE}$)	0,0240	0,0225	0,0208	0,0200
	PROPORTIONAL ABSOLUTE INTAKE	100	125	144	167
	PROPORTIONAL RELATIVE INTAKE	120	113	104	100
B	BODY CONDITION SCORE (1-5)	2,9	2,7	2,6	2,4
C	CONCEPTION RATE (%)	90	85	75	70

EXPLANATORY NOTES:

A Intake of different size animals varies in proportion to Metabolic Size and not actual size

B Body Condition Scores are related to Relative Intake (Eg 2,4 [600kg] x 1,20 = 2,9 [300kg])

C Conception Rates relate to Body Condition Score as determined by Meaker, J (1991)

FIGURE 6.1: *INTAKE AND REQUIREMENT OF DIFFERENT COW SIZES ON LOW QUALITY GRAZING (54% TDN).*

The net result is that the smaller frame animal has an unfair advantage. It is also true to say that the larger frame animal is genetically handicapped because its intake of nutrients falls short of what is required in order for it to grow in proportion to its size. Large frame cattle require "high octane" grass or additional concentrate feed in order to be "productive".

Maturity Rate and not absolute growth rate (ADG) or size (weaning weight, 12 month weight, 18 month weight) should be used as a measure of overall efficiency. Whereas absolute growth, size and Phase C Feed Conversion Efficiency (FCE) are negatively correlated to body condition on veld Maturity Rate is positively correlated. Genetically determined body condition is the major determinant of practical fertility.

BODY CONDITION IS THE A TO Z OF CATTLE BREEDING AND MANAGEMENT

If you asked my late uncle, oom Jerry, what the most important underlying attribute required by cattle is, his answer would have been unequivocally: Body Condition. If you ask an animal scientist from the South African ARC Animal Improvement Institute the same question, the answer will be unequivocally: Phase C Feed Conversion Efficiency. What these scientists don't seem to realise is that oom Jerry, and other ranchers in the pre performance testing and supplementary feeding era, visually selected for body condition because that is what determined survival. Indirectly they selected for efficiency of grass conversion. ARC animal scientists select for feedlot feed conversion efficiency using a mathematically flawed model which results in lean and "efficient" cattle requiring more than just supplementary feeding in order to be "productive". The result is that oom Jerry's cattle were genetically predisposed to good body condition whilst the scientists' cattle are genetically predisposed to poor body condition.

Body condition is the A to Z of cattle breeding and management. **Everything** else is only important in as much as it influences, or is influenced by, body condition. Body condition is a reflection of overall adaptation, an indicator of grass conversion efficiency and the main determinant of practical fertility. **It is essential.** If it doesn't come from breeding it has to come from feeding.

PHOTO 6.1: *Body condition is the A to Z of cattle breeding and management.* **Everything** *else is only important in as much as it influences, or is influenced by, body condition.* **It is essential**. *If it doesn't come from breeding it has to come from feeding.*

LEAN AND "EFFICIENT" IS VERY COSTLY

Animals mature physiologically (degree of fatness) at different rates. This applies to different breeds as well as animals within a breed or herd. The faster maturing animals are fatter at any given age. Fat meat contains much more energy than lean meat. So, at any stage there is more energy stored in a kilogram of gain for an early maturing animal than a late maturing animal. This has serious implications for performance testing.

The South African National Beef Performance Testing Scheme, run under the auspices of the Agricultural Research Council, is regarded by some as the best in the world. In their more sophisticated Phase C test, growth is measured as average daily gain (ADG) and efficiency of feed conversion (FCE) as kilograms of feed required for 1kg gain. Bulls from varying backgrounds, but similar age, are collectively tested in a feedlot where both individual feed intake and weight gain are recorded over a period of time. At the end of the test bulls are ranked (Gold, Silver, Bronze and Sub-Merit) according to ADG and FCE with the "poorest" performers being slaughtered.

On the surface everything appears to be straight forward. The leaner, more "efficient" bulls are being selected. It costs less to produce lean meat and the housewife apparently prefers lean meat. Since the late 1960s lean has been the in thing and fat bad in cattle breeding circles. But, as the saying goes: "Meanwhile, back at the ranch........... ".

A major reason why a bull would require less feed to gain a kilogram is that the gain consists more of lean meat and water than fat resulting in less energy required and stored per unit of gain. The result is that Gold Merit bulls are leaner than Sub-Merit bulls. It doesn't take much figuring out to realise that lean bulls will sire lean cows and heifers and that lean cows and heifers do not cycle. Scientists from the ARC Animal Improvement Institute need to understand that you must compare apples with apples and not apples with pears. They also need to understand that accurate measurement (BLUP) of an inappropriate criterion (FCE) is not very clever.

If cattle are bred to be lean and "efficient" they will require better nutrition in order to be "productive" (fertile). The cost to the producer is incalculable but can be gauged from the extraordinary measures (irrigated pasture and two month weaning) some stud breeders resort to in order to increase the reconception rate of first calvers (Landbouweekblad, 26 January 2007). If you breed or use, lean and "efficient" bulls, be prepared to feed your cows.

BODY CONDITION IS THE MAJOR DETERMINANT OF PRACTICAL FERTILITY

Prof. Jan Bonsma popularised the concept of hormonal balance and its influence on fertility. This was very positive. He was also instrumental in popularising the concept of lean and "efficient". This proved to be disastrous (See Photos: 16.12 and 16.13).

There is a big difference between academic fertility and practical fertility. A very masculine bull with a perfect hormonal balance possesses an extremely important determinant of fertility which is of academic value unless he can also sire female progeny that, in addition to being very feminine (hormonally balanced), are genetically predisposed to good body condition. Practical fertility requires sexually early maturing heifers that are also physiologically (fatness) early maturing and capable of maintaining body condition. This allows two year calving on veld and high reconception rates with minimal assistance from man. Such fertility has a positive influence on the bottom line.

There has been, and still is, discrimination against so-called "pony-type" (short, masculine and very early maturing) bulls. They are short due to the fact that they are physiologically early maturing (small frame) as well as being sexually early maturing (high testosterone levels at an early age limits frame size). These are precisely the bulls that will sire cows and heifers with a high degree of practical fertility.

Animal scientists as well as breed judges and inspectors would be half right if they selected bulls solely on visual appraisal for masculinity without considering Phase C growth and feed conversion efficiency. But they are much more than half wrong by doing so. As a matter of fact, we would be far better off without the current performance tests and herd inspections. Rubbish? Why, then, are the "unimproved" breeds superior to the "improved" breeds in veld tests?

FAT IS A DROUGHT RESERVE

Energy is what drives the world. Cattle require energy to perform. Fat is energy. All cattle that have evolved under conditions of poor nutrition are early maturing and capable of fattening at an early age and lower weight. Cattle that have evolved in seasonal rainfall areas with an extended dry season and periodic prolonged drought are not only early maturing but are also able to fatten quickly with the ability to store additional fat. This stored fat is essential for production and survival during periods of paucity.

The value of this fat which is also stored in the humps of the African Zebu (Angoni and Boran) becomes apparent when animals on poor grazing start drawing on energy reserves. Animals with no energy reserves in the form of fat will lose much more weight than fat animals when mobilising the same amount of energy. This is because of the lower energy content of lean meat. That is why the slower growing, but faster maturing, "unimproved" cattle are more productive on veld than the faster growing, but slower maturing, lean, "efficient" and "improved" breeds.

BODY CONDITION IS A REFLECTION OF GRASS CONVERSION EFFICIENCY

Regardless of its performance, an animal requires a certain amount of energy in order to maintain weight and stay alive. If it is able to ingest more than this maintenance requirement it gains weight. An increase in intake makes more energy available for growth. The faster an animal grows relative to its size the more efficient the growth and the faster it fattens (matures). Therefore, everything else being equal, the fattest (most mature) animal at a given age is the most efficient. Body condition is a far better indicator of grass conversion efficiency than ADG and feedlot FCE.

GOOD BODY CONDITION ENHANCES THE IMMUNE SYSTEM

Animals in good condition are less likely to become ill and are able to limit parasite infestation. The opposite is also true – animals in poor body condition are highly likely to succumb to diseases that were suppressed by a good immune system, such as those transmitted by ticks. Cow body condition at calving influences the quality of colostrum in milk with a consequent long term influence on progeny health.

BODY CONDITION IS DETERMINED BY RELATIVE INTAKE

Relative intake refers to an animal's daily grass intake relative to its size (intake: size). This is described in detail elsewhere, but needs to be mentioned here. Relative intake is dependent on frame size, climatic adaptation, resistance to parasites/diseases and individual appetite.

THE BEST ANIMALS ARE BEING SLAUGHTERED IN THE NAME OF SCIENCE

BULL'S DESTINY DETERMINED BY WHITE SPOT

We are all familiar with the subjective decisions, fuelled by ego and ignorance, made by show judges. This could be dismissed as the result of superstition from a bygone era. However, how does one explain similar irrational decisions being made by persons professing to be breeding along scientific lines? I personally witnessed Prof. Jan Bonsma culling a particularly well muscled Bonsmara bull, at the completion of a Phase C test, on the grounds of a white spot on its forehead.

Similar decisions are being made by breed inspectors on a daily basis. This is superstition and not science.

PHOTO 6.2: *This Bar Z Veldmaster bull symbolises two opposing views. From the viewpoint of "modern scientific breeding" he is too "pony-like", indicating poor feedlot growth and the tendency to fatten too early. He also has a white spot on his forehead. From the viewpoint of veld productivity he is the epitome of grass conversion efficiency (8-in-5 package). At the age of four years his two-year-old daughters had calves on the ground thanks to inherently good body condition and a perfect hormonal balance. He is also naturally polled.*

THE FASTEST MATURING BULLS ARE BEING SLAUGHTERED

Current selection practices based on weaning weight, yearling weight and ADG or Indices and BLUP derived EPDs (Expected Progeny Differences) based on these figures exclude progeny from smaller frame animals as breeding material. This is particularly true in the case of bulls (See Figure 6.2). Calves with Indices of 85 or 68 for weaning weight or 80 and 60 for yearling weight, or the equivalent negative EPDs, are unquestionably culled. Yet, these calves have been produced at equal efficiency, with the smallest frame heifer (300kg mature size) requiring a gain of only 30kg (150 + 30 = 180) from weaning to reach puberty (60% mature) as a yearling, making it the most productive (fertile) on veld.

In any herd there is a large variation in frame size. The average cow size in South Africa is approximately 500kg. This means the larger cows will weigh 600kg and the smaller ones 400kg. Heifer progeny of equal maturity at 12 months (60% of mature weight) will vary between 240kg and 360kg. This is a massive difference of 120kg (50%) for heifers of similar maturity and potential productivity. What is the chance that a breeder or adviser, using "modern breeding methods", will select a bull weighing 30% to 50% less with an index of 80 or 60 and a highly negative EPD at 12 months? Yet, these bulls' female progeny will be better veld adapted (body condition), and more fertile, requiring a much smaller gain from weaning to 12 months (30 and 53kg vs.110kg) in order to reach sexual maturity. As lactating cows they will also be in better body condition resulting in higher reconception rates.

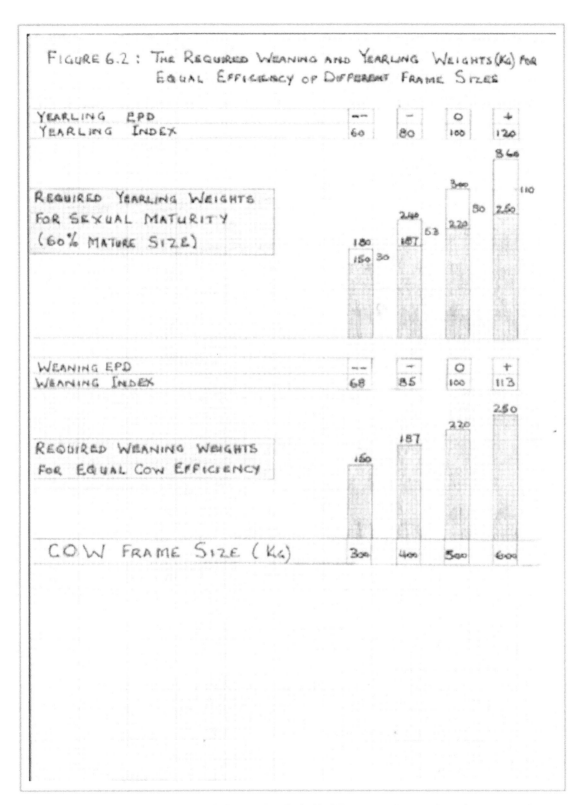

FIGURE 6.2: *THE REQUIRED WEANING AND YEARLING WEIGHTS (KG) FOR EQUAL EFFICIENCY OF DIFFERENT FRAME SIZES.*

In addition to the egotistical whims of show judges and breed inspectors cattle face the errors of "modern breeding methods". There is absolutely no doubt that the result is poor veld productivity. Progeny from Show Champions and Gold Merit bulls require an improved environment in order to be "productive". Bulls with potentially the most veld productive progeny are being slaughtered in the name of science. The slogan, "Man Must Measure", loses its intended meaning when you measure the wrong things.

THERE IS NO UNIVERSALLY SUPERIOR GENOTYPE

Due to the fact that environments differ in terms of nutrition, climate, parasites and diseases and that different morphological and physiological attributes are required for adaptation there is no universally adapted genotype. Environments dictate the appropriate genotype. A genotype adapted to a particular environment will be less adapted to another environment and completely unadapted to the opposite environment. This has important implications for selection.

Cattle need to be selected in a similar, or poorer, environment to where they are going to produce. This is one of the reasons why conventional stud breeding in an artificial environment is such a farce. It is totally unprofessional, and to a large degree dishonest, to breed and performance test cattle under artificial conditions (irrigated pasture, energy-based feed, 2 month weaning onto calf meal, total parasite control, etc.) and then sell breeding stock to the commercial producer under the pretense that they will make him more money. Similarly, it is dishonest to suggest, or imply, that BLUP analysis will allow accurate genetic comparisons of all economically important traits across all environments. A trait such as fertility is determined by hormonal balance (largely unaffected by environment) and body condition (largely a reflection of environmental adaptation). It is therefore subjected to genotype x environment interaction.

Animals performing well in one environment will perform poorly in a different environment. This will be reflected in fertility. No mathematical model can correct for this in order to allow animals to be compared across environments with regard to traits that are subjected to genotype x environment interaction.

PHOTO 6.3: *Daughter, Antoinette, with an animal adapted to a very cold environment.*

The physical and physiological characteristics of these two animals make them adapted to very different environments. Switching environments would result in very poor body condition, if not death, for both animals. Practical fertility is largely dependent on body condition. These opposing genotypes cannot be universally fertile. Neither can BLUP-derived EPDs bridge this chasm.

PHOTO 6.4: *An animal adapted to a hot and humid tropical environment with high ultraviolet radiation and a high incidence of parasites.*

IMPROVED ANIMAL PERFORMANCE CANNOT COMPENSATE FOR A LOW STOCKING RATE

When the focus is on cattle, as in conventional stud breeding, we lose sight of a much bigger picture. When we are obsessed with the superficial as well as high individual performance, measured in absolute terms, there is no way that maximum sustainable profit/ha (or return on investment) can be attained. Individually high productivity, focussing on grass conversion efficiency and fertility, is essential. But, even this cannot compensate for the low stocking rates accepted as the norm.

GOAL: PRODUCTION/ANIMAL OR PROFIT/HA?

Nothing changes a person's mind as much as a buyer becoming a seller, or vice versa. Similarly, nothing changes a rancher's mind as much as a change in focus from production/animal to profit/ha. Apart from being a good business decision, a goal of maximum **sustainable** profit requires highly productive veld. This entails managing hoofs and mouths in such a manner that each animal has a positive influence on all the natural processes in the ecosystem. This means, in general terms, the more cattle the greater the productivity of veld and the higher the profit. This is contrary to conventional management where each additional animal increases the negative effect on individual performance and the ecosystem. In such a situation the reasoning would be to increase absolute production per animal, even to the extent of decreasing stocking rate. Such thinking results in a lower return on investment and dismisses the only practical means of improving veld, particularly in seasonal rainfall environments.

STOCKING RATE IS THE MOST IMPORTANT FACTOR DETERMINING PROFIT

The Charter Estate Trial run over a 7 year period in Zimbabwe during the 1970s clearly showed that stocking rate was the most important factor determining ranch profitability (profit/ha or return on capital investment). Where double the number of cows were run (1 herd/16 paddocks), in order to fully utilise sourveld, profit/ha increased by 28% although calving rate declined by 13% and weaning weight by 10% relative to the conservatively stocked (selectively grazed) control herd (1 herd/ 4 paddocks). The cattle used in this trial were Sussex/Afrikaner crossbreds which performed well under conventional management (low stocking rate, selective grazing). The drop in individual performance that was experienced at a doubling of stocking rate could, in retrospect, have been ameliorated by using a better genotype (eg. Mashona/Boran), more paddocks/herd (in the order of 1000 to 2000), calving in sync with veld quality (calving close to mid-rains) in addition to a higher level of supplementation (a body condition score increase of 0.2 on a scale of 1 – 5 would increase calving rate to that of the control herd).

These factors will be considered in the comparisons made in Figure 6.3. This will also highlight the fact that higher stocking rates become even more important where land prices are very high relative to the conventionally accepted stocking rate.

FIGURE 6.3: THE IMPORTANCE OF STOCKING RATE IN DETERMINING RANCH PROFITABILITY

RANCH SIZE   = 1000 ha
RANCH VALUE   = $1 000 000
STOCKING RATE   = 4 ha / 600kg Cow

MANAGEMENT SYSTEM		CONVENTIONAL		SUSTAINABLE	
		V1	V2	V3	V4
STOCKING RATE (RELATIVE)		X 1	X 2	X 2	X 3
STOCKING RATE (ha /600kg Cow)		4	2	2	1,33
COW SIZE (Kg)		600	600	300	300
PADDOCKS / HERD		4	16	2000	2010
H 1	TOTAL COWS	250	500	835	1262
H 2	CALVING RATE (%)	80	67	90	90
H 3	BODY CONDITION SCORE (1-5)	2,6	2,4	2,9	2,9
H 4	WEANING WEIGHT (Kg)	250	226	150	150
H 5	TOTAL WEANERS	200	335	752	1127
H 6	TOTAL WEANING WEIGHT (Kg)	50 000	75 275	112 800	169 050
H 7	TOTAL WEANER VALUE ($)	100 000	150 750	225 600	338 100
H 8	TOTAL DIRECT COST ($)	30 000	60 000	60 000	90 000
H 9	TOTAL GROSS MARGIN ($)	70 000	90 750	165 600	248 100
H 10	GROSS MARGIN / COW ($)	280	182	198	198
H 11	GROSS MARGIN / HECTARE ($)	70	91	166	248
H 12	CAPITAL : LAND ($)	1 000 000	1 000 000	1 000 000	1 000 000
H 13	: COWS ($)	225 000	450 000	375 750	563 400
H 14	: TOTAL ($)	1 225 000	1 450 000	1 375 750	1 563 400
H 15	RETURN (GROSS MARGIN / CAPITAL) (%)	5,7	6,3	12,0	15,9
H 16	CALVING % REQD. FOR RETURN OF 5,7%	80	68	55	48
H 17	CALVING % REQD. FOR RETURN OF 15,9%	180	129	111	90

FIGURE 6.3: *THE IMPORTANCE OF STOCKING RATE IN DETERMINING RANCH PROFITABILITY.*

IS A 200% CALVING RATE POSSIBLE?

Figure 6.3 represents a comparison between different systems of ranch management in regard to profitability (Gross Margin/ha and Return on Investment). The difference between the systems is based on three variables: cow size, stocking rate and the number of paddocks per herd. The figures in vertical columns V1 and V2 are based on the 7 year Charter Estate Trial. Column V1 represents the Control (Charter management) and column V2 represents Short Duration Grazing (so-called "Savory" system). The figures in columns V3 and V4 represent a sustainable system and are based on an actual doubling and trebling of stocking rate on similar veld (Pumula, Karoi; See Chapter 22: SEEING IS BELIEVING) together with assumptions based on intake and body condition of different cow sizes (Nowhere have the variables of cow size and number of paddocks/herd been tested relative to profit/ha).

The comparisons are based on the total annual production of weaner calves on 1000ha of ranch land in South Africa with a conventional stocking rate of 1 Large Stock Unit/4ha and a value of $1,000,000. Readers are encouraged to do the same comparison based on their own figures.

The following is an explanation of how the figures in Figure 6.3 have been calculated:

- Horizontal line H1 refers to the total number of cows in a system. The Charter Estate Control represented in column V1 at a stocking rate of 1/4ha carries 250 cows weighing approximately 600kg each. The Short Duration Grazing system (V2), at double stocking rate, carries 500 cows of similar size (600kg). In this example of a sustainable system, cow size is taken to be 300kg necessitating a conversion of cow numbers relative to the amount of grass eaten by cows of different size. The average 600kg cow eats as much as 1.67 cows weighing 300kg (See Figure 6.1). Thus, the number of smaller cows represented in column V3 is 835 (250 x 2 x 1.67) and in column V4 is 1252 (250 x 3 x 1.67).

- On line H2 are the respective calving rates for V1 and V2 (actual) and for V3 and V4 (assumption based on body condition).

- Line H3 represents Body Condition Score (BCS) on a scale of 1- 5. In column V1 and V2 the BCS is correlated to actual calving rate. In columns V3 and V4 the BCS is based on the 20% higher relative intake of 300kg cows as opposed to 600kg cows (2.4 x 1.2 = 2.9) which would relate to a 90% calving rate (See Figure 6.1).

-       The weaning weight of 150kg from a 300kg cow and 250kg from a 600kg cow (H4) relate to equal cow efficiency based on weaning weight relative to intake (See Figure 6.1).

-       Horizontal line H7 gives the value of weaned calf based on weaning weight and a sale value of $2.00/kg.

-       H8 refers to total direct costs that vary in direct proportion to the number of cows (relative stocking rate). This is based on 30% (100,000 x 30/100) of the turnover of the Control (V1). Thus, in columns V3 and V4 the figure of 30,000 is multiplied by 2 and 3 respectively. Although, strictly speaking, cow numbers are higher than a factor of 2 and 3 this is disregarded because of the smaller cow size (less supplement per cow required to achieve similar body condition).

-       Gross margin (H9) is calculated by subtracting direct costs from total calf value (turnover).

-       Land value (H12) is the same for all systems. The capital invested in cows is based on cow weight and a live weight value of $1.50/kg. The total capital investment is shown in H14.

-       The annual return on investment (H15) is calculated as a percentage by dividing total gross margin with total capital investment.

-       Lines H16 and H17 refer to the calving rates required to attain the lowest (5.7%) and highest (15.9%) returns on investment.

The results from Figure 6.3 clearly show that stocking rate is by far the most important determinant of ranch profitability. Where double the number of conventionally bred cows were carried on the same land area, calving rate dropped from 80% to 67%, yet gross margin and return on investment increased (H9 and H15). In order for conventional management (conservative stocking rate and selective grazing) to compete with sustainable management (drastically increased stocking rate and inherently high body condition) cows will have to produce twins. If the academics at universities do not accept the possibility of increasing stocking rate then they will have to assist ranchers in raising twins. It is as simple as that.

FERTILITY: FEEDING OR BREEDING?

Fertility (stemming from inherently good body condition) is, without a doubt, the most important characteristic required by cattle. It is essential for the growth and survival of a population, it is a major determinant of ranch profitability and it reflects overall adaptation as seen in body condition resulting from a high relative intake. Does it make sense that the driving force of nature would be lowly heritable? Is fertility 90% feeding (environment) and only 10% breeding as suggested by the textbooks and believed by the academics? Does "survival of the fittest" not apply in this case?

MOST COWS ARE POTENTIALLY VERY FERTILE

The majority of cows, barring disease, are capable of calving regularly from two years of age. However, some would require feedlot nutrition to achieve this whilst others require only veld with no, or little, assistance from man. The common denominator is good body condition. The one group achieves this via the feed bag whereas the other group is able to achieve good body condition on veld via inheritance. Some animals are genetically programmed (large frame, late maturing) for poor body condition; others are genetically programmed (small frame, early maturing) for good body condition. If we say fertility is lowly heritable then we say body condition (frame size, climatic adaptation, resistance to parasites/diseases and appetite) is also lowly heritable since it is the major determinant of fertility. If body condition was lowly heritable then "survival of the fittest" would not apply and selection for adaptation would be impossible.

FERTILITY IS DETERMINED BY BODY CONDITION AND HORMONES

Apart from body condition, fertility is determined by the balance between sex hormones and growth hormones. An animal reaches sexual maturity when there is a decrease in growth hormones and an increase in sex hormones. Concomitantly there is a decrease in the growth of all the long bones (legs, jaws, transverse spinal processes) and ultimately a cessation of growth. The age at which this occurs as well as the decreased potential frame size (genetic) is determined by the level of sex hormones (testosterone in the bull and oestrogen in the heifer). These hormones are also responsible for the development of the secondary sexual characteristics. The implication of the modifying effect of hormones on appearance, frame size (as opposed to weight) and growth is still not fully appreciated 50 years after the concept was popularised by Prof. Jan Bonsma. Many of those who do select for a good hormonal balance fail to appreciate the importance of body condition. Hence, the low practical fertility (reflected by the absence of 2 year calving and poor reconception rates on veld) of most herds, particularly amongst the "improved "breeds.

In both bulls and cows there are visual indicators (secondary sexual characteristics) of fertility. But, in the cow its value is historic and not predictive. In other words, it is possible to visually assess a cow's fertility record in terms of age at first calving and subsequent calving record, but it is not possible to predict a yearling heifer's future calving record. The man hasn't been born who can do this. However, it is an easy matter to breed all heifers at 14/15 months and rank them individually in terms of fertility after the second calving.

With bulls it is much easier to assess testosterone levels at an early age and there is merit in doing this, particularly when looking at the opposite ends of the spectrum. Some bulls develop much earlier, sexually, than other bulls. Apart from the visual indicators of masculinity (testis, hump/crest, defined muscling, darkening in colour) some bull calves will follow cows on heat and try to mount them. Those that do this at an earlier age are sexually earlier maturing. They will sire heifers that are sexually earlier maturing and who only require a genetic predisposition for good body condition (early physiological maturity) in order to be able to calve at two years of age on the veld. In the absence of appropriate performance figures, it is advisable to evaluate a bull solely in terms of testosterone level and physiological maturity (8-in-5 package vs. 9-in-10 package).

High testosterone levels in a bull are indicated by muscling and muscle definition, high length: height ratio (relatively short legs), wide thighs as viewed from behind, deep chest, thick neck, large hump/crest, coarse hair on the sheath and tail switch and often on the neck, darkening of the forequarter and lower hip area and an "aggressive" (not necessarily bad temper) attitude. This "aggressive" attitude is also manifested in bulls herding cows, pawing the ground, fighting anthills and trees (bald forehead) and giving a sideway look at potential adversaries.

Cows with a good hormonal balance (history of early and regular calving) have a wedge shaped (dairy type) appearance viewed from the side – deep hindquarter and shallow forequarter. They have the appearance of walking downhill with a prominent and loose shoulder blade that is level with, or higher than, the spinal processes. In zebu breeds the hump of a fertile cow is much smaller than that of less fertile cows. A fertile beef cow may be well fleshed but will show no sign of muscling although she will pass muscling on to her male progeny.

It is well worth noting the sexual dimorphism that occurs in hormonally balanced herds. This refers to the large difference between bulls and cows in terms of weight, muscling and other secondary sex characteristics. It is very apparent in the African breeds with the exception of many Afrikaner herds that have been "improved" by show judges and breed inspectors. In the case of many Afrikaner cattle, selection for a good looking head ("mooi kop en horings") in bulls and a prominent hump in cows (a hormonally balanced Afrikaner cow will have no hump) led to a hormonal imbalance. This has resulted in low fertility in the Afrikaner breed despite them excelling in the other determinant of fertility – good body condition. However, there are individual animals in some herds that do have a good hormonal balance as manifested in heifers being bred at 14/15 months and calving at the age of two years.

The value of understanding the modifying influence of hormones in cattle lies less in the ability to visually assess fertility and more in appreciating the effect of hormones on growth/size and morphology. Clarity on this subject would lie in resting many misconceptions. Foremost amongst these is the general prejudice against stocky, very early maturing bulls referred to as "pony-types". This is largely a result of an overreaction to the problems of dwarfism that occurred in many studs in America during the 1950s when active selection for smaller cattle took place. A different problem arose in the 1980s, after a decade of selecting for large frame cattle ("leggier" cattle "with a lot of sky underneath"), when it became apparent that they were sexually later maturing and generally less fertile. The response was to include scrotal circumference as an additional selection criterion.

Anyone with some understanding of the relationship between hormones and size should have realised the futility, and stupidity, of such an exercise. It can be compared to a person willfully taking poison (selecting for a large frame) and then taking an antidote (selecting for a larger scrotum) to try and counteract the effect of the poison (poor fertility). It must be similarly clear to anyone with a full understanding of the influence of hormones, as well as maturity rate (size at a given age as a proportion of mature size) being an indicator of grass conversion efficiency, that the "pony type" bull is the antithesis of the slab-sided, frame-scored freak ("draadkar"). One is the result of early physiological and sexual maturity; the other the result of late physiological and sexual maturity. The one is veld productive; the other is a man made freak with no place in the real world.

It must be emphasised that the stocky bulls (8-in-5 packages) referred to here are the result of very high levels of testosterone (well muscled and relatively short in the leg) and a very fast growth rate relative to mature frame size (efficient grass conversion). **Nowhere is active selection for smaller, lighter cattle advocated.** By using appropriate criteria, selection will be for faster growth, within the optimum frame size for an environment, as determined by nature and not man. Such bulls will produce cows that are extremely fertile and veld productive – the opposite of what we have as the norm today.

There is currently, in South Africa at least, much talk about selecting for larger pelvic openings in order to facilitate calving ease. I understand the reasoning behind this when trying to limit calving problems in conventional breeds – particularly heifers calving for the first time. I also have no problem with this approach as a temporary measure. The problem I foresee is when bulls are selected for a large pelvis. The consequence will inevitably be hormonally imbalanced bulls and cows – a large pelvis is not a masculine trait. This is reminiscent of selecting for large frame bulls during the frame-scoring era and trying to counter the negative hormonal effects by selecting for scrotal circumference. Surely it would be more prudent to select directly for calving ease which is dependent on more than just pelvic size.

CULLING IS NOT SELECTION

All stud breeders say they select for fertility, even though the majority regard fertility as being lowly heritable. This is generally done by culling the 10 – 20% cows and heifers that do not conceive. This is not selection. It is the same as claiming to select for growth when culling the 10 – 20% slowest growing bulls and breeding with the remaining 80 – 90%. Major genetic change is brought about by the bull. Unless bulls can be accurately ranked in terms of practical fertility (hormonal balance **and** body condition), and the most fertile used (high selection differential), there is no selection for fertility.

FERTILE COWS AND MEDIOCRE BULLS

All cows in a herd of 100 cows of the same age that have calved annually from the age of two years are, in regard to phenotype, (determined by genotype and environment) equally fertile. But, are they genetically equally fertile? If environmental conditions had, historically, been more difficult (shorter breeding season, less supplementary feed) it is obvious that some cows would not have had the same reproductive record. If conditions were very difficult, only a few would have a 100% calving record. Conditions could have been so bad that only one cow would remain with a perfect record. This means that, in terms of genotype, the 100 cows vary on a continuum from the most fertile to the least fertile even though they are on the surface (phenotype) equally fertile (See Figure 6.4).

FIGURE 6.4: The Profile of Genetically Determined Fertility in a Herd

Bull Fertility Score

Cow Fertility Score	10	9	8	7	6	5	4	3	2	1
10	10			8½						
9	9½			8						
8	9			7½						
7	8½			7						
6	8			6½						
5	7½			6						
4	7			5½						
3	6½			5						
2	6			4½						
1	5½			4						

FIGURE 6.4: *THE PROFILE OF GENETICALLY DETERMINED FERTILITY IN A HERD.*

Let us now consider any herd of 100 cows. Without any record or knowledge of each cow one thing is certain. There are some extremely fertile cows that are hormonally balanced and adapted (to a degree) to their environment. The question is: Are the bulls being used of a similar genotype to the 10% most fertile cows or will the resulting progeny prove to be inferior to their dams in regard to fertility? The bulls being selected on current selection criteria (Fertility Score of 7?) may lead to an improvement on the poorer cows, but there is no doubt that the progeny from the best cows will be inferior to their dams. In effect, selection is toward a mediocre average. It is essential to identify the bulls with the highest practical fertility (Fertility Score of 10) that are capable of complementing the best cows and improving on the poorer ones.

FERTILITY IS HIGHLY HERITABLE

The heritability of a trait, in simple terms, refers to the portion of observed (measured) variation between animals that can be passed on from one generation to the next. It is expressed as a percentage or fraction. For example, a selection criterion (there are different criteria to measure a trait) with a heritability of 10% means that only 10% of the measured difference between animals can be attributed to genes; the other 90% is due to environmental differences that, in the case of fertility, can be date of calving (seasonal differences in nutrition), age at calving, feeding, management earlier in life and others. Selection progress based on this measurement will be slow. If the criterion to measure cow fertility, such as calving rate, is lowly heritable (10%) does that mean cow fertility is lowly heritable?

It is very unfortunate that the perception that fertility is 90% feeding and 10% breeding has become entrenched in most minds. It is erroneous and misleading. Let us consider a herd of hormonally balanced and adapted Ngunis and a herd of hormonally balanced and less adapted Bonsmaras grazing tropical sourveld. There is no doubt that, with minimal supplementation, infrequent dipping and no internal parasite control, the Nguni herd will have a far higher calving rate. The reason for this is better body condition due to superior overall adaptation. Are the determinants of cow body condition (milk production, frame size, climatic adaptation, resistance to parasites/diseases and appetite) not highly heritable? If they are highly heritable it must be possible to increase the Bonsmara herd's fertility (body condition) through selection, particularly if there is sufficient genetic variation in addition to the occurrence of positive mutations.

Some will argue that increasing supplementation, decreasing stocking rate and improving parasite control will also improve the Bonsmara's fertility (body condition). This is true and is the current state of Bonsmara herds in general, but body condition attained through feeding is not heritable. It is the easier solution if your goal is biased towards production per animal and you are not concerned about ecological and economical sustainability. However, it does not detract from the fact that selection for fertility can be very effective. What is required are genetically discerning selection criteria that can enable the breeder to rank (score) bulls and cows from the most fertile to the least fertile in terms of practical fertility.

CALVE IN THE RAINS FOR MAXIMUM FERTILITY

The general recommendation is for cows to calve 6 – 8 weeks before the start of the rains. The reasoning behind this is that you will wean a heavy calf (true) and that the cow will cycle early due to a rising plane of nutrition (classroom theory in low latitude environments) resulting in a high reconception rate. Where is the logic in planning calving to occur at a time when nutrition is the poorest and the cow's nutritional requirements the highest, unless weaning weight has preference over fertility? Body condition and nutrition at calving have the greatest influence on post calving anoestrous period (period from calving to first heat) and reconception rate. It is not surprising, therefore, that current breeding season's are long (3 – 12 months) and feeding levels excessive in order to achieve acceptable reconception rates.

In all seasonal rainfall areas there is a strong relationship between date of calving relative to the middle of the rains and post calving anoestrous period. Generally speaking, the average cow will have a three – quarter day shorter anoestrous period for each day calving occurs closer to mid – rains. Over a conventional 90 day calving season this equates to a 60 - 70 day shorter inter calving period for a cow calving at the end of the calving season as opposed to the beginning.

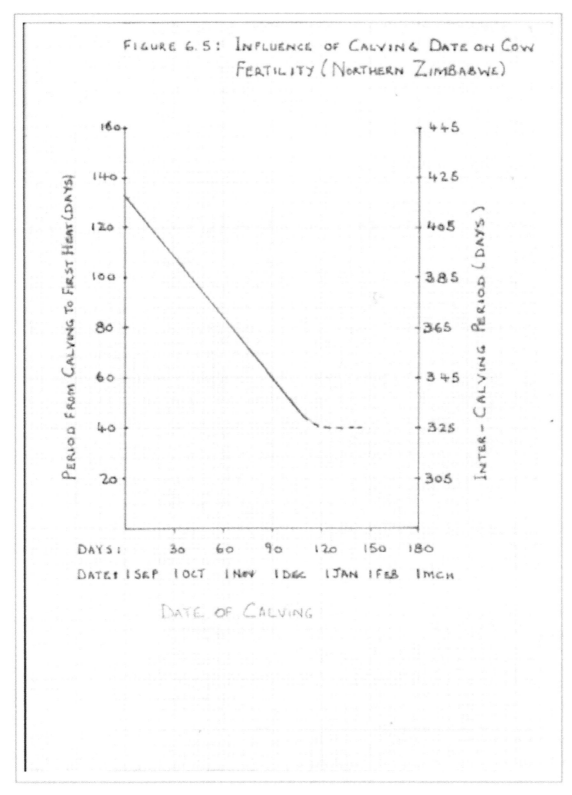

FIGURE 6.5: *INFLUENCE OF CALVING DATE ON COW FERTILITY (NORTHERN ZIMBABWE).*

Figure 6.5 is constructed from actual and extrapolated (dotted line) results obtained in Northern Zimbabwe (veld plus protein supplement) where the seasonality of rainfall is very strong (approximately 80% of rain falling in a 3 - 4 month period). For each day a cow calved closer to mid – rains (January) her post calving anoestrous period, and potential ICP, decreased by 0.81 days. This means that the average anoestrous period for cows calving mid - December is approximately 40 days as opposed to approximately 130 days if the same cows calved early September. This is solely due to the fact that in one instance cows calve on good veld (green grass) and in the other instance they calve on poor veld (dry grass). The general recommendation in this environment is to time calving to start in September.

Under the conditions prevailing in this example no cow would be able to maintain an ICP close to 365 days (conceiving approximately 80 days after calving) when calving in September. With a restricted calving/breeding season of 3 months the most fertile cows (mainly better body condition) would settle into a November calving pattern whilst the poorer cows would be unable to cycle early enough in order to reconceive. The result is a long breeding season with poor reconception rates.

Increased supplementation (or better veld) and a better genotype (inherently good body condition) will decrease the anoestrous period (intercept on the Y axis) at any particular date but will not eliminate the seasonal effect – earlier calving cows will still have longer anoestrous periods.

If calving were to occur from mid - December to the end of January (42 day breeding season starting 1 March) the majority of cows (80% plus) would cycle before the start of the breeding season, the average ICP would be 365 days for consecutive calving cows and reconception rates would be in excess of 85%. Such a situation allows for extremely effective A.I. with, or without, synchronisation. Whether A.I. or natural service is practised, the majority of calves will be born within 3 weeks.

Although environments differ as to when appropriate calving/breeding should occur, officially recommended dates are out of sync with seasonally varying nutrition. This applies, in particular, to cow reconception and yearling heifer conception (higher 14/15 month weights). Early season calving does favour weaning weight but this advantage is lost by yearling age with lower 14/15 month weights. Productivity, ease of management as well as effective A.I. and supplementation are improved by delaying calving date relative to the current dates.

There is no major cattle production environment where a 42 day breeding season is not practically feasible. Such a situation allows an improvement in fertility through feeding (green grass) and breeding. The breeding aspect is discussed fully later (See Chapters 7: THE MOST PROFITABLE BEEF ANIMAL, 8: BREEDING FOR PROFIT and 9: SELECTING FOR FERTILITY).

PHOTOS 6.5 and 6.6 are of Bar Z 85-139 taken at 15 months and 5 years of age. They show the predictive value of assessing hormonal balance in a young bull. The high level of testosterone, as reflected in secondary sexual characteristics, was apparent at an early age and confirmed at maturity. The differences in sexual maturity of individual bulls can be assessed visually, to a degree, at a young age. This can be of value in terms of selection but is not a panacea for practical fertility which is also dependent on inherently good body condition. (See Chapter 9: SELECTING FOR FERTILITY).

PHOTOS 6.7 and 6.8 are of the same animal (Bar Z 87-60) as an 8-month-old calf (left) and a 2-year-old cow (right). It is clear that, in the female, fertility is not predictive. There are few, if any, secondary sexual characteristics that could have made this cow stand out from her peers at an early age. As is the case with her peers that calved early, her appearance only changed radically after becoming pregnant. The degree of female fertility, from least fertile to most fertile, can only be assessed after calving.

(See Chapter 9: SELECTING FOR FERTILITY).

PHOTO 6.9: *An Afrikaner bull with an exceptionally high level of testosterone. This is indicated by his secondary sex characteristics such as muscle definition, colour differentiation and particularly his behaviour – herding cows, pawing the ground and constant bellowing. It is very important to differentiate between poor temperament and "aggressiveness" associated with high testosterone level.*

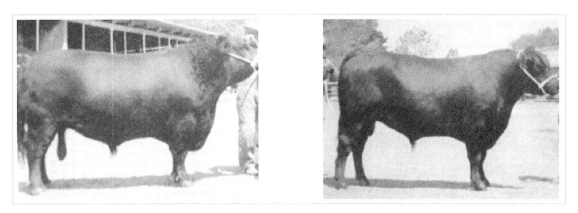

PHOTOS 6.10 and *6.11* *(taken in 1983) are of two bulls from the same herd that symbolise opposing breeding philosophies and that represent opposites in terms of physiological and sexual maturity. The differences in secondary sexual characteristics are very obvious. The "fertile ox" on the right clearly has under developed testes – the result of selecting for a large frame (hip height). The bull on the left has a stocky appearance (8-in-5 type) due to a combination of early physiological and sexual maturity – the antithesis of the "fertile ox".*

PHOTO 6.12 *is a rear view of the above two bulls and shows the difference in frame size (hip height) and masculinity. The fertile ox (right) is much taller with wide hips (feminine trait). According to the*

breeder, and in line with the fashion at the time, the animal on the left was deemed inferior. To quote the misinformed breeder: "The problem with this bull (left) is that he is sexually early maturing and stops growing at an early age. The modern requirement is for larger cattle that will fatten at a heavy weight".

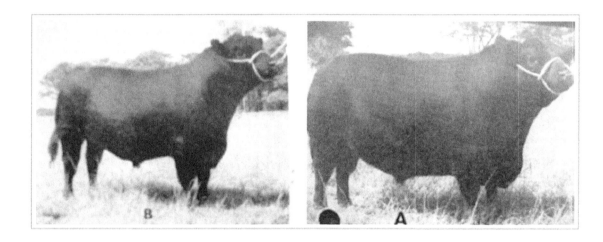

PHOTOS 6.13 *and* **6.14** *are of two bulls that were described by Prof. Jan Bonsma in 1970 as being desirable (left) and undesirable (right). The breeder, Mr. Black, disagreed and was of the opinion that Bull A (right) was the better one. In Prof. Bonsma's opinion Bull A was hormonally imbalanced as evidenced by greater fat deposition. In defence, Mr. Black said that this was due to over-feeding for the show ring and that the bull in question had a very fertile mother. I believe Mr. Black to have been right in this case. The problem with a hormonally balanced but* **lean** *bull (B on left) is that his female progeny, although hormonally balanced, will have inherently poor body condition and therefore lower practical fertility. The "lean and efficient" approach by Prof. Bonsma was, in my opinion, disastrous. It led to the breeding of cattle that require extra feed in order to be "productive".*

PHOTOS 6.15 and 6.16 are of two hormonally balanced bulls with different degrees of practical fertility. The bull on the left is physiologically much earlier maturing (fatter) with the ability to sire females with greater practical fertility (hormonal balance and inherent body condition). However, with current performance tests and selection criteria the bull on the right will be selected for breeding.

PHOTOS 6.17 and 6.18 depict two bulls with very different maturity rates and practical fertility. The 2-year-old bull on the left is extremely masculine (defined muscling) and relatively small frame – the result of generations of selection for early maturity (15-month breeding). Despite this bull's high degree of practical fertility, breed inspectors from a "scientifically improved breed" would discriminate against him on the basis of a twisted scrotum. The late maturing "bull" (right) with the fluffy tail and infantile testes was declared a champion and an example of what cattlemen should strive for. This is another illustration of man's perverted thinking.

PHOTOS 6.19 *and* **6.20**

PHOTOS 6.21 *and* **6.22**

The bulls pictured are all examples of early physiological and sexual maturity. They are the product of fast relative growth and a high level of testosterone. This can be seen in their muscle: bone ratio, muscle definition and high length: height ratio. There is a positive correlation between the mentioned desirable attributes and a tight skin and sheath. These bulls will sire female progeny with a higher level of practical fertility in line with their nutritional adaptation.

PHOTOS 6.23 *and* **6.24** *show 8-year-old cows, each with their 7th calf and pregnant again with their 8th. Note the typical wedge shape, thin neck and "loose" shoulder blades.*

PHOTOS 6.25 and 6.26

PHOTOS 6.27 and 6.28

These 2-year-old cows have several common attributes. They are all wedge shaped with thin, feminine necks and "loose" shoulder blades that are as high as, or higher than, their thoracic vertebrae. They also have sloping rumps and, viewed from the back, "roofy" rumps which enable easy calving.

PHOTOS 6.29 and **6.30** are of a 2-year-old cow shortly after calving and 5 months into the dry season at weaning. Calving in good body condition in the middle of the wet season (800 – 1000mm in 4 months), she conceived within the first 21 days of a 42 day breeding season.

PHOTOS 6.31 and ***6.32***: *The good body condition of these 2-year-old cows is a reflection of genotype and the time when they calved. Contrary to convention they calved during mid-rains on tropical sourveld and weaned their calves 5 months into the dry season. Both cows conceived within a 42 day breeding season to produce their second calf at the age of 3 years.*

CROSSBRED BULLS ARE SUPERIOR TO PUREBRED BULLS

Everyone agrees that the use of crossbred cows is positive, yet virtually everyone is of the opinion that the use of crossbred bulls is retrogressive. Where does this perverted thinking come from? Stud breeders trying to protect their interests and colluding academics who feel they need to toe the line? There is absolutely no indication or proof that crossbred bulls per se are inferior to purebred bulls.

Part of the superstition around the use of crossbred bulls stems from an erroneous extrapolation of the results of simple Mendelian inheritance (few genes involved) where segregation occurs for qualitative traits (eg. colour) when breeding F1 (first cross) to F1. Such inheritance does not apply to the economically important quantitative traits such as size (maturity type/body condition), muscle: bone ratio, milk production, appetite, climatic adaptation and resistance to parasites/diseases that are largely dependent on the additive action of many genes. Another misconception is that it is not possible to accurately determine the genetic value of crossbred bulls due to the effect of hybrid vigour (partly non-additive gene action) masking the heritability (largely additive gene action) of a trait. This may be true to an extent when comparing purebreds with crossbreds. This definitely does not preclude accurate comparison of crossbred bulls, particularly if they are of a similar genotype.

GREATER HYBRID VIGOUR

Crossbred bulls have greater hybrid vigour than purebred bulls, particularly in respect of fertility. If hybrid vigour is dependent on the degree of heterozygosity, as currently believed, then crossbred bulls will generate more hybrid vigour than purebred bulls when bred to the appropriate cows. For example, a crossbred bull composed of breeds A and B will result in greater hybrid vigour when bred to cows from breed C than using a bull from either breed A or B. Even greater hybrid vigour will result by breeding crossbred bull A/B to crossbred cows C/D. And, 75% of this hybrid vigour can be maintained in subsequent generations when closing such a herd (See: Gregory, K.E and Cundiff, L.V; J. Anim. Sci., Vol. 51, No.5, 1980).

OPTIMISING ADAPTATION, PRODUCTIVE EFFICIENCY AND HYBRID VIGOUR

In conventional crossbreeding (rotational or terminal) it is not possible to optimise adaptation, productive efficiency and hybrid vigour across all generations with the use of purebred bulls. This is because of a large variation in genotype between generations due to the variation in adaptive and productive traits of the different breed bulls used. For example, when using Brahman and Angus in a rotational crossbreeding system in the tropics certain generations will lack either adaptation or productivity, in both bulls and cows, with the possible exception of the first generation cows. This problem can be solved easily and hybrid vigour increased by using the appropriate crossbred bull. A good option would be to use Nguni/ Boran bulls on the first cross Brahman/Angus cows. A further improvement, in a harsh environment, would be Brahman/Bonsmara instead of Brahman/Angus.

GREATER SELECTION PROGRESS

Work done by Roy Berg from the University of Alberta in Canada (Personal Communication, 1983) shows very clearly that crossing crossbreds is more productive and that **selection within a crossbred herd, using crossbred bulls on crossbred cows, is much more effective than in a purebred herd**. When selecting for yearling weight, the annual increase in weight over a 16 year period was 2.0kg for the purebred Hereford control herd and 4.4kg for the crossbred herd. The difference in yearling weight, in favour of the crossbreds, increased from 33% at the start of the trial to 68% after 16 years of selection. This is contrary to current stud breeding propaganda.

The reason for a greater selection response in a closed crossbred population is probably due to greater genetic variation allowing superior gene combinations (combining productive and adaptive traits). In addition to this, there is greater hybrid vigour generated by combining several breeds and the fact that it is possible to retain up to 75% of this hybrid vigour in a closed herd with a crossbred foundation.

EASIER HERD MANAGEMENT

When using purebred bulls in a rotational crossbreeding system the number of breeding herds needed increases in relation to the number of breeds being used. This is not the case when using crossbred bulls as only two herds would be required when four breeds are involved. A composite combining four breeds would require one herd. This allows for much easier management and less infrastructural development.

PHOTOS 6.33 and **6.34**: *Both these bulls are the product of a crossbred bull on a crossbred cow.*

EFFECTIVE SELECTION IS NOT POSSIBLE WITHOUT INBREEDING

There is no doubt that the kind of inbreeding that was done in studs in the past was detrimental. It cannot be otherwise, when one considers the ineffectiveness of conventional selection in regard to "survival of the fittest". Where "survival of the prettiest" is practised there is a concentration of genes unrelated to, and probably in conflict with, adaptation. But, that does not mean that a concentration of desirable genes is bad. You cannot select effectively without some form of inbreeding. The challenge is to ensure that only desirable genes are concentrated by using appropriate selection criteria and relying on natural selection.

***PHOTOS 6.35** and **6.36:** The positive effects of inbreeding when nature determines what is desirable. Pictured on the left is a magnificent Lasater Beefmaster bull resulting from selection in a herd that has been closed for close to 80 years. Selection is such that nature is the judge of what is desirable or not. The photo on the right (Courtesy of Jon Marshall) is of a Hereford herd that has been stranded on one of the Aleutian Islands (close to the Arctic) for a century without human interference. The result has been inbreeding and survival of the fittest. Note the masculinity and meat: bone ratio of the bulls as well as the maternal efficiency of the cows which can be seen from a distance.*

GENES RUN IN THE FAMILY

One cannot get away from the fact that the best animals in any herd are related. With effective selection in a closed herd, or limited population, (inevitable when improving adaptation to a specific environment) inbreeding is inevitable. By minimising the intensity of inbreeding (no sire-daughter or sire-granddaughter mating) and selecting for biological and reproductive efficiency ("survival of the fittest") no problems should be encountered. This is borne out by inbred populations occurring in nature (many populations are highly territorial) as well as cattle populations where nature has been the judge of what is the most desirable (fittest). The Lasater Beefmaster herd in Matheson, Colorado is a prime example of the result of selecting for fitness characteristics in a herd closed for close to 80 years. The late Prof. Jan Bonsma regarded it as "the most functionally efficient herd in the world". What makes this even more remarkable is the fact that this herd, in its current state, grew from a very small population of cows (170?) that remained in 1947 after initiation of a policy of only keeping cows that calved annually from the age of two years.

IS IT INBREEDING OR DEFECT BREEDING?

It is essential that appropriate selection criteria be used, that nature be the judge of what is desirable and that the process of concentrating these genes is accelerated. If inbreeding (linebreeding?) occurs as a consequence of this then that is how it should be. But, if inappropriate criteria are used and inbreeding is practised specifically to concentrate the resulting genes the consequences will be very different. The latter process can be described as defect breeding.

THE "UNIMPROVED" BREEDS COME TO THE RESCUE

Manie and Karin Wessels, located between Frankfort and Vrede in the Free State Province of South Africa, provide a prime example of how the use of an "unimproved" breed rectified the shortcomings of a "scientifically improved" breed. Starting with purebred Bonsmaras (could just as well have been one of many other "improved" breeds) they encountered many problems of poor nutritional adaptation (no hay or crop residue used where such use is the norm in this area) and tick borne diseases. In desperation, and against conventional advice, they bought Nguni ("unimproved" breed) bulls for use on their Bonsmara cows. The result, a few years down the line, is that the females with sufficient Nguni blood are able to breed at 14/15 months (and younger) with the majority (80 – 90%) calving at two years (and younger) and maintaining very high reconception rates (over 80%) on veld with protein supplement. In addition, mortality from tick borne diseases is currently 0.2% without any antibiotic treatment relative to double digit figures in the past with antibiotic treatment.

The value of using "unimproved" breeds to improve the "improved" breeds also applies to herds within a breed. I have personally been involved in advising certain breeders on the breeding of sexually early maturing Afrikaner cattle. The problem with the Afrikaner "improved" by show judges and breed inspectors is a hormonal imbalance resulting in poor fertility. It was possible to locate sexually early maturing cows and bulls, through visual selection, in herds least affected by selection according to breed standards. Such animals were capable of breeding at 14/15 months and calving at two years of age. I have no doubt that very few if any, such animals could have been found in the conventionally bred Afrikaner herds.

PHOTO 6.37: *Two-year-old Nguni x Bonsmara cows with their calves sired by Nguni x Bonsmara bulls in the herd of Manie and Karin Wessels, Free State Province, South Africa. A low calving rate and high mortality has been turned around in one generation. Approximately 80 – 90% of cows calve at the age of two with over 80% conceiving again. Mortality is down from double digits to 0.2%.*

NATURE IS THE FINAL JUDGE

We have inherited once perfectly functioning ecosystems. Natural laws ensured survival of the fittest and harmony between all organisms. Cattle populations that were subjected to these laws have very different characteristics to those that conform to man-made laws. When the laws of nature are flouted a penalty has to be paid. In the case of cattle, where survival of the fittest no longer applies, the environment has to be modified (selective grazing, excessive feed substitutes, antibiotics, dips and de-worming drenches) to ensure survival and "productivity". There is an ever increasing cost in terms of money and environmental deterioration. The only solution is acceptance of the fact that in the long term nature's verdict is final. Deferment is only temporary and the ultimate penalty costlier.

CATTLE BREEDING IS BOTH AN ART AND A SCIENCE

There are three critical decisions a breeder needs to make – the genetic base from which he starts, the bulls used and the subsequent selection that takes place. The first two involve an art that is dependent on human skill gained from acquired knowledge and experience. This is not to be confused with the so-called sixth sense that show judges and breed inspectors supposedly have enabling them to visually evaluate cattle. The third one involves a realisation that natural selection is perfect and that devising methods of reading nature correctly is science in its purest form.

There is an art in deciding which genotype (breed; individuals within a breed) combinations will ultimately result in the ideal animal for a particular environment. There is a science in determining genetically discerning selection criteria and accelerating the process of genetic change to a desirable end.

7. THE MOST PROFITABLE BEEF ANIMAL

The majority of people have an idea of what they **think** a good beef animal should **look** like. This is based on preconceptions arising from superstition and bad science. Do we want show cattle or veld cattle; feedlot performance or veld productivity? Is colour important or not? Is pedigree registration essential? Can BLUP analysis take environment out of the equation completely? It is time cattlemen decided what a good beef animal is. It is time they distinguished between fact and fiction; fantasy and reality; utility and glamour; superstition and science.

There are as many roads to success as there are goals. If a cattleman wants to breed show champions he must be very clear that that is what he is breeding and not veld performers. If he uses centre pivots and early weaning of calves onto calf meal he must inform potential bull buyers that that is what they will require in order to attain acceptable reproduction. An appropriate goal is essential in order to achieve harmony between man, cattle and veld. Such a goal is **maximum sustainable profit/ha**. It is all-encompassing in that it considers both environment (sustainable) and economics (profit). Surely no serious-minded cattleman has a problem with this.

Maximum sustainable profit/ha is not positively influenced by most, if not all, of the characteristics deemed important by stud breeders. Where is the connection between Show Champions or Gold Merit bulls and veld productivity? Does the mere recording of a pedigree (pedigreed purebred vs. unregistered purebred) elevate an animal to a higher level of superiority in terms of veld productivity? Is an SP (Studbook Proper) animal a more efficient grass convertor than an F1, F2, F3 or F4 animal? Are breeds with heavy, lean carcasses of greater value than those that fatten at a younger age and lighter weight? Does the twist of the testicles and a white spot out of place influence the bottom line? These are questions that need to be asked and answered - if not by stud breeders and academics, then by commercial producers.

PHOTOS 7.1 and **7.2**: Is an "improved" stud bull with show ribbons, a recorded pedigree and performance data more productive on veld than a so-called "bosbul" (bush bull/village bull)? Is "survival of the prettiest" preferable to "survival of the fittest? It is time cattlemen differentiate between myth/pseudoscience and fact.

Globally, cattle producing environments differ tremendously. Differences in climate require differences in coat type and pigmentation. Hot environments require a smooth coat whereas cold environments require a woolly coat. Cattle in the high altitude tropics need good pigment. Differences in nutrition also have their demands. Low "octane" grass is best utilised by smaller frame cattle that have a high relative intake. Hot, humid, poor nutrition (fibrous, high heat increment grass) environments result in a greater heat burden and require smaller frame, smoother coated cattle with a larger surface area in order to maintain thermal equilibrium. The point is: **There is no universally superior genotype**.

Environment should dictate the most profitable genotype and not man. The "ideal type of animal", a term used by show judges and breed inspectors, should be determined by environment via the process of natural selection. Only when bearing this in mind can a constructive debate be had in regard to the most profitable beef animal for a particular environment. Let us also keep the words of Tom Lasater in mind when he said: *"Cattle breeding is a relatively simple endeavour. The difficult part is to keep it simple"*.

HIGH RELATIVE INTAKE/GOOD BODY CONDITION/EFFICIENT GRASS CONVERSION

An animal requires a certain amount of food each day in order to maintain weight. Nutrients above this maintenance level are used, in order of priority, for growth, milk production (lactating animals), and fat deposition (conception). Against a background of varying frame sizes and levels of milk production it is obvious that there will be great variation in body condition (practical fertility). This will reflect the efficiency of grass conversion. Everything else being equal, the animal that is capable of the highest grass intake relative to its size will be in the best body condition resulting in the highest fertility and most efficient grass conversion. Cattle need to be **bred** and **managed** for a high relative intake (intake: size). The genetic components are frame size, climatic adaptation, resistance to parasites/diseases and individual appetite.

PHOTO 7.3: *The genetic base for productivity is a high relative intake. The Mashona cow pictured above (Courtesy of Jaime Elizondo) exhibits all the components of a high relative intake – optimum frame size (fleshing), overall adaptation (sub-tropical environment of Florida) and a large appetite (aggressive grazer). This is evident in her body condition and extended rumen. This inherently good body condition together with a perfect hormonal balance allows this cow to have a high degree of practical fertility.*

FRAME SIZE

As previously explained intake is not in proportion to size, but to a function of size (metabolic size) which decreases, in relation to size, the larger the animal. This means that, regardless of everything else, larger animals have a lower relative intake. This translates into poorer body condition (lower fertility) and less efficient grass conversion. The average smaller frame animal has a larger relative intake than the average larger frame animal giving it the edge in terms of body condition and fertility. The average 600kg cow has a 67% (not 100% higher) higher absolute intake than the average 300kg cow, yet the smaller cow has, on average, a 20% higher relative intake and consequently a 20% better body condition.

Due to the fact that conventional selection favours larger frame animals, selecting smaller frame animals will have a positive effect (in the current situation) on veld productivity. In the long term, however, selection criteria need to be used that reflect efficiency of grass conversion, regardless of frame size.

CLIMATIC ADAPTATION

A climatically unadapted animal is like a poorly tuned car engine. It performs badly and is expensive to run. Such an animal has a low daily intake in a hot environment (raised body temperature) or uses energy in order to maintain optimum body temperature in a cold environment. In both instances efficiency of grass conversion is decreased. Climatic factors that adversely affect intake, together with the appropriate genotypes, are:

HEAT

Cattle in hot environments require a smooth coat. Numerous sweat glands also aid heat dissipation. Since some breeds of cattle that have developed in hot environments have a loose skin it obviously suggests that this also aids heat dissipation. However, this does not mean that a loose skin *per se* is an adaptive requirement for hot environments as evidenced by the highly heat tolerant, yet tight-skinned breeds of Bos Taurus origin (eg : Senepol from the Carribean Islands, Romosinuano from equatorial Colombia and the N'Dama from equatorial West Africa).

COLD

Cattle in cold environments generally require a woolly coat with an inner heat retaining layer. Some high latitude (further from the equator) continental environments also have hot summers, in which case cattle need to shed long winter coats. This can generally happen with the European Bos Taurus breeds owing to the large difference in daylight length between winter and summer (photoperiodic effect) at these latitudes. In the high altitude tropics, where differences in daylight are small, European origin cattle need to be genetically smoother coated in order to cope with less photoperiodic effect and relatively high temperatures.

An additional factor aiding cold tolerance is body fat. Fat is a good source of readily available energy and a subcutaneous layer of fat may also insulate the body from cold. This could explain the apparent cold tolerance of the Boran (African Zebu) in the eastern Highveld area of South Africa.

SOLAR RADIATION

Both infrared as well as ultraviolet radiation is higher in the tropics. Ultraviolet radiation is also higher at higher altitude. In order to protect cattle from sunburn and skin cancer caused by ultraviolet radiation the exposed areas of skin need to be pigmented. There is evidence that lighter coloured cattle can reflect a larger amount of infrared rays resulting in lower skin temperature and greater heat tolerance. This would put them at an advantage in environments with extremely high infrared radiation such as tropical deserts. This has to be seen in perspective, however, as such environments are limited. Most ranching areas in hot environments are probably less colour prescriptive. Whatever the situation, using the appropriate selection criteria for grass conversion efficiency will result in the right colour.

HUMIDITY

High humidity increases the heat burden of unadapted cattle in a hot environment. An aggravating factor in such environments is the high fibre content of fast growing tropical grasses that release more heat when rumen fermentation occurs. This is very evident in the high altitude (relatively cooler) Central African tropics where even Zebu crosses with the European breeds suffer tropical degeneration. This is not the case in dry, hot environments with cool nights and low fibre grasses such as Namibia. This phenomenon was borne out to me during a visit to south-western Texas where I witnessed black Angus cattle grazing at noon on a very hot day. The same cattle would be seeking shade in a cooler environment such as the Zimbabwe Highveld with its higher humidity, high fibre grasses and lower photoperiodic effect (woollier summer coat).

RAIN

Overcast weather with virtually continuous rain for extended periods will adversely affect intake with some animals being affected more than others. This is probably due to the direct effect of rain on grazing time as well as an indirect effect on nutrition, foot-rot, parasites and diseases. It is difficult to prescribe the appropriate genotype except to say that cattle with dark hooves are, in general, more resistant to foot-rot. Again, direct selection for grass conversion efficiency (maturity rate, body condition) will result in the appropriate genotype since there is a large variation in animals' response to stressful conditions. One case I encountered bears this out. The growth of one group of contemporary bulls, of apparently equal adaptation, ranged between 15kg and 90kg over a very wet period.

PHOTOPERIOD

The effect on hair shedding between winter and summer at different latitudes in relation to temperature adaptation has been mentioned. Another effect of photoperiod has to do with hormone levels. At latitude 17 degrees south of the equator (Pumula, Karoi) twice the number of embryos were collected during September/October (lengthening daylight) as opposed to March/April (shortening daylight) indicating optimum hormone levels with increasing day length. However, maximum practical fertility was attained by breeding in March/April (optimum cow body condition) indicating the overriding influence of nutrition in this environment. At higher latitudes (further from the equator,) photoperiod and its influence on hormone levels as well as nutrition (low fibre grass and good spring nutrition) may very well have a large influence on practical fertility. This could account for the fact that cows can achieve a high reconception rate in such environments even though they may calve in poor body condition. Cow body condition at calving in the tropics needs to be much better in order to achieve the same degree of fertility.

RESISTANCE TO PARASITES AND DISEASES

There is variation between breeds and animals within a breed in terms of resistance to parasites and diseases. Work done in South Africa (Scholtz M.M. et al: Onderstepoort J. Vet. Res. 1999) shows the relative resistance of three breeds to ticks. When not dipped, the exotic Hereford had more than six times the number of ticks than the indigenous Nguni. The Bonsmara, where the Afrikaner's resistance has been diluted with exotic breeds, had four times more ticks than the Nguni. This is also reflected in similar weaning weights for non-dipped Bonsmaras (medium size breed) and Ngunis (small breed). Practical experience, supported by research, also indicates greater genetic resistance of African breeds to tick-borne diseases as well as screw-worm. The same applies to the internal parasites each genotype has encountered in its evolution. This should not be a revelation, since these animals are the survivors of centuries of exposure to parasites and their accompanying diseases.

INDIVIDUAL APPETITE

Individuals of the same frame size and equal overall adaptation will still vary in terms of relative intake due to differences in individual appetite. That this has a strong genetic base and that it is entirely due to differences in urgency of grazing and grazing time was shown by New Zealand researchers in the 1950s (Hancock, J : New Zealand J. of Sci. and Tech. 1950). The most capable pair of identical twins grazed for 555 minutes (9 hours 15 minutes) per day while the least capable pair only grazed for 379 minutes (6 hours 19 minutes) - a difference of 46% in grazing time, resulting in an equivalent difference in intake. Experience with UltraHigh Density Grazing (1000 – 5000 cattle/ha) bears out this genetic difference in aggressiveness of grazing. Certain individuals will always be grazing at the front of a moving electric wire whilst others remain at the back. This difference in their behaviour is also reflected in their body condition.

HORMONAL BALANCE

A major determinant of fertility, together with body condition, is a favourable hormonal balance (high level of sex hormones). Bulls must have a high level of testosterone and heifers a high level of oestrogen at an early age. This will be reflected in their morphology and secondary sexual characteristics. The most obvious difference between hormonally balanced and hormonally imbalanced herds is the degree of sexual dimorphism between males and females, the smaller frame size of fertile animals and the early sexual activity of bull calves.

PHOTO 7.4 *(Courtesy of Kobus van der Linde): Hormonal balance refers to a high degree of sex hormones – predominantly testosterone in the bull and oestrogen in the cow. This is reflected in a high degree of sexual dimorphism (masculinity in the bull and femininity in the cow) as evidenced by this family of Afrikaner cattle.*

HIGH MEAT: BONE RATIO

The problem with assessing conformation is making the unimportant important. This is a trade mark of show judges and breed inspectors. The twist of the testicles in bulls has no negative effect on fertility, yet such bulls are discriminated against. Nature allows a large variation between extremes in terms of the angle of the hind leg. But, man, in his wisdom, decides to impose stringent standards unrelated to productivity. Bulls are selected in terms of the proportion of high-priced cuts when it has been demonstrated that there is no difference between the average Jersey and the average Limousin. The meat: bone ratio varies a great deal, but not the proportion of different muscles.

Apart from the really important functional characteristics (eg. ease of calving, equal size testes, pigment around the eyes, no serious structural defect, prominent secondary sexual characteristics) the only other important aspect of conformation is meat: bone ratio. An animal with a high meat: bone ratio will yield a carcase with a high dressing percentage. A 5% better dressing percentage will result in approximately a 10% heavier carcase and 10% higher monetary return for animals of the same live weight. Other important aspects of a high meat: bone ratio in bulls is that it is an indication of early sexual maturity and a fast maturity rate (grass conversion efficiency/body condition). In general, a high meat: bone ratio is correlated to a relatively fine bone structure, tight sheath in bulls and a neat udder with small teats in cows.

PHOTO 7.5: *(Courtesy of Christo Mouton): The importance of meat: bone ratio in bulls cannot be overemphasised. It indicates inherently good fleshing and a high level of testosterone as depicted by this magnificent Afrikaner bull. The female counterpart exhibits fleshing (not defined muscling) and femininity (See Photo 7.3).*

OPTIMUM MILK

A beef cow with too much milk requires dairy cow nutrition in order to calve regularly. An overly poor weaner heifer (low calf: cow ratio and not light weight) will not achieve the target yearling maturity for it to conceive and calve at two years of age. What is required is a weaning weight, at 7 – 8 months, approximately 50% of mature weight. This is achieved much easier for smaller frame cows owing to their larger relative intake and consequently proportionally greater amount of nutrients available for milk production.

PHOTO 7.6: *A 370kg Bar Z Veldmaster cow with her 215kg calf. Although she weaned a calf weighing 56% of her own weight her milk production can be considered to be optimum relative to nutrition when judged by her body condition and the fact that she was pregnant. A cow with a much larger frame would not be able to achieve the same maternal efficiency under a regime of Non-Selective Grazing and treble stocking rate on sourveld (low "octane" grass). The amount of milk she would need to produce a calf 56% her own weight would not allow sufficient body condition in order to conceive whilst lactating.*

EASY - CARE

Natural selection results in cattle that can survive adverse conditions. Conventional selection in an artificial environment results in cattle human intervention. We require cattle that can convert grass efficiently into meat with the minimum inputs in respect of labour, feed, antibiotics, dips and drenches.

TEMPERAMENT

Cattle require a calm temperament. They must be responsive to commands from man. Cows need to be good mothers. Bulls must be dominant over cows. A good herd instinct is a big advantage in terms of handling, particularly where UltraHigh Density Grazing is practised.

CALVING EASE

Apart from a disease pandemic, nothing causes as much distress amongst ranchers as difficult births. Without the slightest doubt, conventional selection is to blame for the abnormally high rate of difficult births experienced by many herds and breeds. This is related to issues such as size, body shape (flat rump as opposed to sloping and "roofy" rump) and other body dimensions (width of body and size of head).

HEALTHY IMMUNE SYSTEM

Cattle that are genetically programmed for good body condition in a particular environment also have a healthy immune system. They will also exhibit greater genetic resistance to parasites and diseases.

POLLEDNESS

The dehorning of cattle is generally a traumatic exercise. If this is done during hot, humid conditions there is also an increase in the incidence of screw-worm attack. Polled cattle eliminate the need (ease of handling and reduced bruising) to dehorn.

TIGHT SHEATH

All the arguments for bulls to have a "moderate" sheath do not hold water. There is a correlation between a sloppy sheath and poor muscle: bone ratio, bottle teats and curved cervix in cows as well as late sexual and physiological maturity in general. All a "moderate" sheath does is decrease the incidence, or severity, of these undesirable characteristics. Bulls with a large, sloppy, pendulous sheath (large prepuce opening and not necessarily a large navel fold) are also inclined to injury from thorns, grass seed and ticks. Selecting for a tight sheath will result in cattle with fewer structural defects. A tight sheath (small prepuce opening) is positively related to a fast maturity rate (grass conversion efficiency).

PIGMENT

Pigment around the eyes and other exposed body parts is essential in environments with high ultraviolet radiation. Dark, hard hooves (related to overall pigmentation) are more resistant to foot-rot.

8. BREEDING FOR PROFIT

Apart from the selection criteria to be employed, the most important decisions a cattleman can make in terms of breeding are the breed or breeds to be used, the appropriate genotype within a breed and the breeding system to be followed. This involves a knowledge of the various breeds (or genotypes), choosing a creative breeding system and the art of matching genotype to environment.

BREEDS

The choice of a certain breed over another must be determined, firstly, by the environment. This relates to overall adaptation. The second consideration is productivity as determined by hormonal balance, milk, meat: bone ratio and ease of management. Although there is tremendous variation within a breed, the following synopsis of breeds is an attempt to highlight their positive and negative attributes. It must be emphasised that even though a breed may generally be negative for a certain attribute there will be individuals that will be positive. For example, although the hormonal balance of the Afrikaner breed has been negatively affected by selection there are individuals with an appropriate balance as evidenced by heifers calving at two years of age. Another example is the Tuli and Senepol breeds that are polled and generally have good veld productivity, but with many bulls exhibiting preputal (sheath) prolapse (related to the polled factor in many breeds). The solution is to select the right bulls.

AFRICAN ZEBU

All Zebu (Bos Indicus) cattle are distinguished by a hump (large in bulls and small in cows) that is positioned over the shoulder in contrast to Bos Taurus cattle that have a muscular crest in bulls (not developed in hormonally balanced cows) that is situated on the neck. Sanga cattle are intermediate

BORAN

The outstanding attribute of the Boran is its fattening ability and resultant drought tolerance. This ability is the result of evolution in a desert environment (southern Ethiopia and northern Kenya) and makes it the obvious choice for arid environments and areas with a long dry season. These fat reserves apparently allow it to cope with low temperatures as evidenced by its survival of very cold winters in parts of South Africa.

The other positives of the Boran are a high physiological maturity rate, heat resistance, good pigment, tick and tick borne disease resistance as well as a very strong herd instinct. There is a great deal of variation in terms of conformation/structural soundness, temperament and sexual maturity. Some bulls have extremely good sheaths (small prepuce opening) whilst others have poor sheaths. There is also a tendency for late sexual maturity. There are enough good animals to eliminate the negatives if breeders wish to do so. Polled animals do occur.

PHOTOS 8.1 and **8.2:** *Boran bull and cow.*

ANGONI

The Angoni (East African Zebu, Malawi Zebu) can best be described as a "cousin" of the Boran that developed under very different climatic, parasite/disease and nutritional conditions. Like the Boran they have an Asiatic origin and have evolved in Africa for centuries. Unlike the Boran they have developed in a seasonally high rainfall, humid environment with generally poor nutrition and a high incidence of ticks, blood-sucking insects, internal parasites and the accompanying diseases.

They are found in eastern Zambia, Malawi, Tanzania, northern Mozambique and in small numbers in Zimbabwe. They are different from the Boran by being much smaller, more tick/parasite/disease resistant (personal experience and information gleaned from herdsmen in Zambia), having a sleeker coat and perfect sheaths in bulls. They also have good fattening ability, but possibly not to the same extent as the Boran. They have a very strong herd instinct and cows have very good maternal ability. Like the Boran, poor temperament and late sexual maturity do occur, but with sufficient variation to allow positive selection. Polled animals are found.

PHOTOS 8.3 and **8.4**: *Angoni bull and cow.*

AFRICAN SANGA

The Sanga is regarded by some as mainly of Bos Taurus origin. In reality they are probably a combination of Bos Taurus and Bos Indicus. The Afrikaner, which is classified as a Sanga, shows a very strong Zebu influence (large hump, loose skin, fattening ability) whilst the Tuli shows more Bos Taurus influence (smaller hump and occurrence of preputal prolapse which is a feature of polled Bos Taurus cattle).

NGUNI

The Nguni is, without any doubt, the hardiest and most parasite and disease resistant breed in South Africa. Together with a good hormonal balance, these attributes also make it the breed with the highest practical fertility in South Africa. A big problem is that most animal scientists do not publicly acknowledge this (How can an "unimproved" breed be superior to a scientifically "improved" breed?). The annually published results of the ARC Performance Testing Scheme do not do justice to the superiority of the Nguni due to the fact that Nguni herds, on average, produce under much more adverse conditions (nutrition, parasite control) than the other breeds.

An even bigger problem is the fact that Nguni breeders themselves do not take their breed seriously enough. Which serious-minded commercial producer will buy bulls from a breed whose breeders bull throughout the year (it is regarded as natural for cows to choose when to calve), neglect to dehorn (horns are natural and indicate breed purity) and select for out-of-the-ordinary colour markings? This is in addition to the fact that the Nguni is a small breed and apparently not suitable for the feedlot. The truth is that the right type of Nguni (high meat: bone ratio and, to a lesser extent, a more acceptable colour/pigment) with good leadership could revolutionise cattle production in South Africa and other parts of the world.

The positives of the Nguni are a high degree of parasite/disease resistance, extremely good nutritional adaptation/body condition (survivors of extremely adverse conditions), a generally good temperament and early sexual maturity. The negatives are a generally poor meat: bone ratio and, to a degree, a commercially unacceptable colour (Perceptions favour a solid colour). There are well muscled and solid coloured (well pigmented) bulls that can be used.

There are other Nguni related breeds in southern and central Africa such as the Landim from Mozambique, the so-called Namibian Sanga, the Mashona from Zimbabwe and the Tonga from Zimbabwe and Zambia. The Mashona will be discussed separately due to the fact that it has had a different history in terms of selection starting in the mid-1900s.

PHOTOS 8.5 and **8.6**: *Nguni bull and cow.*

MASHONA

The cattle currently recognised as Mashona were developed by commercial ranchers in Zimbabwe starting from indigenous stock in 1941. The two breeders who, independent of each other, initiated the breeding project are F.B Willoughby and E.A.B. McLeod. What distinguishes the commercially bred Mashona from its Nguni counterpart in South Africa is that selection emphasised a solid colour (black or red), polled cattle and a relatively high meat: bone ratio (Mashonas and their crosses have won carcase competitions) in addition to productive characteristics such as milk and fertility (unfortunately breeding herds did not emphasise two-year calving).

Fortunately the inherent practical fertility of the breed was retained as evidenced by the superiority of the Mashona in crossbreeding trials at Matopos research station. Under difficult, sub-tropical sourveld conditions the Mashona maintained a calving rate of 77% over a 7 year period. The closest rival was the Tuli at 70%. In terms of productivity (annual production of weaned calf/500kg cow weight) the Mashona surpassed its closest rivals, the Tuli and Brahman, by approximately 20%. The Afrikaner was surpassed by 55% (Tawonezvi, H.P.R. et al. 1988: Animal Production: 47 p. 361-367).

The Mashona does have its faults, but they are few. They are inclined to have weepy eyes developing into opthalmia. There is a moderate meat: bone ratio. Its strong points are tropical adaptation, nutritional adaptation (good fattening ability), resistance to ticks, internal parasites and certain diseases, good temperament, poll without prepuce problems in bulls, near optimum milk and early sexual maturity (good hormonal balance). The Mashona is a good example of an inherently productive breed being made commercially attractive through the foresight of a few dedicated breeders. It is very unfortunate that most of the herds have been decimated by the recent Zimbabwe land seizures. On the positive side, though, there are purebred animals in the USA and Australia.

PHOTOS 8.7 and **8.8**: *Mashona bull and cow.*

TULI

The breed as it is known worldwide is also a Zimbabwe creation. It was developed from indigenous stock from the dry south-western sweetveld of the country by a Land Development Officer (Len Harvey) working at the Tuli Breeding Station. Commercial ranchers were later involved in increasing numbers. The end result is a popular breed that has spread to South Africa (largest gene pool) and other countries in Africa as well as overseas to Australia, North America and Latin America.

The strong points of the Tuli are high fertility with early sexual maturity, very good meat: bone ratio, good milk and a generally good temperament. The weak points are prepuce problems in some bulls, bulgy eyes in some cattle (inclined to develop opthalmia) and light coloured animals with poor pigment. There is unfortunately a tendency to select for larger size resulting in poorer nutritional adaptation. There is also anecdotal evidence that tick, internal parasite and disease resistance is less than that of the Mashona and Nguni.

PHOTOS 8.9 and **8.10**: *Tuli bull and cow.*

AFRIKANER

The present day Afrikaner is an anomaly amongst Sangas owing to its low fertility on a breed basis. This is due to a hormonal imbalance created by man. Without this problem, the Afrikaner would be the most popular Sanga breed in South Africa and elsewhere in the world. It is adapted to a hot environment with many animals having a very good meat: bone ratio, good milk production, fattening ability is second only to the Boran and temperament is generally good. The solid red colour and few structural defects (probably least of all the Sanga breeds) make it commercially attractive. The only question mark, apart from fertility, is its adaptation to very wet conditions owing to the fact that it developed in a dry environment. The amber coloured hoof of the majority of animals may be susceptible to foot-rot under such conditions.

The development of the Afrikaner over the last century is a case study of the importance of hormonal balance and how glamour, breed politics, ego and ignorance can, for all intents and purposes, destroy a breed. Studying old photographs shows clearly that cows from the 1920s looked very different to the show winners of the 1960s and later. The early cows had very small humps as opposed to the masculine humps and proportionately larger forequarters of later years. This reflected the hormonal imbalance bred into the breed as evidenced by the effeminate bulls ("mooi kop") of the later period. The fertility problem in the Afrikaner breed is **hormonal and man-made**.

I am privileged to be involved with some Afrikaner breeders who are intent on rectifying this hormonal imbalance. It is very fortunate that there are still some herds that, for various reasons, were not as negatively affected by shows and breed inspections. It has been possible to identify animals with a perfect hormonal balance within these herds – sexually early maturing bulls and cows calving at two plus three years of age. These animals look very different to the show prize winners of the 1960s to 1980s – short, thickset, masculine bulls and very feminine cows with no hump. Hopefully these breeders will set a new trend that will lead to the breeding of a truly veld productive Afrikaner that will be sought after by commercial beef producers in Africa, Australia and the Americas.

PHOTOS 8.11** and **8.12: *Afrikaner bull and cow.*

DRAKENSBERGER

The Drakensberger is a South African breed of mixed origin (Indigenous/European) that is considered to be indigenous and found mainly in the Eastern Highveld region where winters are very cold. Although not a true Sanga it is included here because it does have attributes that are considered to be similar. There is variation, but generally speaking they are veld productive, particularly in the colder regions. This breed definitely has potential for use in other regions of the world (USA, Australia) where there is a large difference between winter and summer temperatures.

PHOTOS 8.13 and **8.14**: *Drakensberger bull and cow.*

ASIAN ZEBU

BRAHMAN

The Brahman is basically a Zebu composite developed in the USA and is one of the breeds that have been most adversely affected by the fad for large frame. This is particularly true of the herds in the USA. Amongst these animals the Red Brahman has been worst affected. The result is that, in general, these cattle are the antithesis of early maturity (sexual and physiological). If one adds structural defects such as a large, sloppy sheath (prepuce problems) in bulls and "bottle teats" in cows as well as poor temperament to the mix the result is extremely poor cattle. Fortunately, however, this is not the end of the story. There are many herds of a different type of Brahman found mainly in Latin America, Australia and Africa.

There must be a reason why the Brahman has become so popular in all the ranching areas of the world. It is a tropically adapted breed and as such combines well with breeds of European origin resulting in highly productive cattle. Apart from many crossbreds, the Brahman is a major ingredient of several composites such as the Beefmaster, Brangus, Braford, Charbray, Droughtmaster and Simbra.

Although the Brahman is sexually later maturing and thus considered less fertile it performed very well in crossbreeding trials at Matopos Research Station in Zimbabwe. As a purebred, and in terms of calving rate, it was second only to the very fertile Mashona and on a par with the Tuli which is also considered to be fertile. Selection for early sexual maturity will enhance the Brahman's fertility. This is borne out by a breeding programme at Belmont Research Station in Australia where selection for scrotal circumference in bulls has resulted in heifers being bred at 14/15 months for two-year calving.

The positives of the physiologically early maturing type of Brahman are a very good meat: bone ratio (amongst the non-European breeds Brahmans are some of the best muscled), parasite/disease resistance, good maternal ability and milk as well as an intelligent character (responsive to handling/training). What needs to be added is early sexual maturity, in which case we will have an animal that will be on a par with the Sanga in terms of practical fertility and with a possible edge in terms of crossing ability (hybrid vigour and complementarity). The large frame ("draadkar") type is a man-made freak and has no place on cattle ranches.

NELORE

The Nelore is one of the components of the Brahman and is the dominant breed in tropical South America. It is fine boned with much smaller ears and less loose skin than the typical zebu. The result is a tighter sheath and high meat: bone ratio in some herds. They have recently been used to improve these attributes in the Brahman. Relative to the Brahman, they are said to be better adapted to poor nutrition. Temperament is generally poor.

INDU–BRAZIL

This is a Brazilian composite of mainly Guzerat and Gir. It is a very large breed with large ears and bulls with pendulous sheaths. They are physiologically and sexually late maturing.

TABAPUA

This is another Brazilian composite consisting of predominantly Nelore breeding. They are fine boned, tight skinned and have a good meat: bone ratio. They are sexually earlier maturing than most other zebus of Asian origin.

GIR

There are milk and beef types. There is a great deal of variation amongst the beef type. All have large ears. Some have a relatively tight skin, fine bone and a good meat: bone ratio. The majority have thick bone, poor meat: bone ratio, a loose skin and bulls with pendulous sheaths.

RED SINDI

A relatively small breed with generally good to very good meat: bone ratio, fine bone, tight skin, bulls with tight sheaths and cows with neat udders and small teats. Cows have a lot of milk and are used for dairy ranching in the drier regions of Brazil. This breed is less popular than the other Asian zebus for beef production due to its relatively small size. However, this should be seen as a positive factor since it will give it the edge in terms of early physiological and sexual maturity. This breed has great potential in increasing veld productivity when crossed with the appropriate breeds.

SAHIWAL

As in the case of the Sindi the Sahiwal is used in dairy ranching. But, unlike the Sindi it is not as suitable for beef production. It has a poorer meat: bone ratio and more loose skin.

TROPICALLY ADAPTED BOS TAURUS

There are several breeds of Taurine origin that, through natural selection, have become tropically adapted. Apart from the Senepol, which partly has an African origin, there are the Criollo (native) breeds of Latin America. Amongst the better known ones are the Romosinuano, Caracu, Blanco Orejinegro, Costeno con Cuernos and Tipo Carora. They are all very smooth coated and highly heat tolerant. The advantage of these breeds is there early sexual maturity (relative to the zebu) and tropical adaptation, making them ideal for crossing with zebu and conventional European breeds.

N'DAMA

Small West African breed of Bos Taurus origin that is adapted to equatorial conditions. They are resistant to trypanosomiasis - a disease transmitted by the tsetse fly. There is a large commercial herd in the Democratic Republic of the Congo.

SENEPOL

The Senepol is a wholly Bos Taurus composite developed in the Carribean from mainly Red Poll and the N'Dama from West Africa. It is sleek coated and highly heat tolerant. Although there is tremendous variation, the Senepol is considered a medium size breed with ample milk that is physiologically and sexually early maturing. All animals are polled with the occurrence of prepuce problems in many bulls. Meat: bone ratio varies tremendously from poor to extremely good. In trials in Texas the Senepol and Tuli produced progeny with very similar characteristics with the Tuli having the edge in terms of fertility.

Appropriately selected Senepols can play a large role in increasing beef production in the tropics. A distinguishing feature is there ability to transmit heat tolerance (all progeny have a smooth coat) to any breed, including woolly-coated European cattle, in addition to the polled factor. Another advantage is the fact that the resultant crosses will all benefit from hybrid vigour.

CARACU

This Brazilian breed is very well muscled and large. Its smooth coat makes it adapted to a hot environment. Cows have more milk than the average beef breed and are also used for dairy ranching.

ROMOSINUANO

A small, polled breed originating from the Sinu valley of Colombia situated at sea level on the equator. They are believed to be the survivors of South European cattle brought to the Americas by the Spanish and Portuguese. They are extremely smooth coated (some animals have very little hair) and heat tolerant.

ADAPTAUR

A Hereford/Shorthorn composite developed at the Belmont Research Station, Rockhampton, Australia. Selection has mainly been for tick resistance resulting in a concomitant increase in tropical adaptation and fertility. Animals are polled with a high degree of prepuce problems amongst bulls. Improvement in tick resistance is to such a degree that crossing selected Adaptaur bulls with the Belmont Red (similar to the Bonsmara) imparts greater tick resistance to the progeny.

CONVENTIONAL COMPOSITES

There is nothing new about composites. The Brahman is a composite, although not generally recognised as such. Many so-called purebreds are in reality composites (crossbred/mixed foundation). The reason why they are not recognised as breeds of mixed foundation is because of the stigma attached to crossbreds/mongrels. Conventional composites resulted from "planned" crossing of Bos Indicus and Bos Taurus breeds in general. Amongst the first are the Santa Gertrudis, Beefmaster, Bonsmara, Braford, Droughtmaster and Brangus. The Simbra is a later addition.

Although there is undoubtedly a great degree of variation between individual herds there is not much difference on a breed basis in terms of productivity. This is borne out by the results published by the South African Agricultural Research Council Livestock Improvement Institute (Beef Breeding in South Africa: Beef

Cattle Performance Testing 1959 – 1999). This raises questions as to the value of the current performance testing programme when the fertility of the Bonsmara, Brangus and Simbra are virtually the same whilst the latter two breeds exhibit higher cow efficiency. Bear in mind that compulsory performance testing has been a feature of the Bonsmara since its inception 80 odd years ago and that the Simbra is a late-comer. It becomes obvious that boundaries between breeds of similar genetic background and selected for similar traits are arbitrary and man-made. It is even more obvious that bull selection in such circumstances should be based on individuality and not breed. In line with this thinking the characteristics of this group of cattle will be discussed as though they are a single genotype.

SANTA GERTRUDIS, BEEFMASTER, BRANGUS, BONSMARA, SIMBRA, etc.

All these breeds were ostensibly bred for production under extensive conditions in a tropical or sub-tropical environment. They are generally heat tolerant, but intermediate in terms of tick resistance. Their disease resistance, particularly to tick-borne diseases, is much lower than that of the African Sanga or Zebu. Being of a medium to large frame and having developed under conditions of good nutrition impacts negatively on their nutritional adaptation. Generally speaking they are sexually relatively early maturing, but practical fertility depends largely on nutritional status. Meat: bone ratio and cow efficiency are good to very good. Temperament is variable.

These breeds can best be employed in breeding systems combining them with the African Zebu and African Sanga. For example, increased milk and muscling can be obtained without losing too much adaptation by combining the Simbra with the Nguni instead of Simmental and Nguni. Similarly, a Bonsmara/Boran combination will deliver better results in certain environments than a British/Boran combination.

BRITISH BEEF BREEDS

Before the Frame Scoring Era of the 1970s and 1980s the British breeds such as the Hereford, Angus and Sussex were early maturing small to medium frame animals. This is the type that can be used fruitfully today in combinations with other tropically adapted breeds to improve veld productivity. The only countries where these animals were valued and where the original type can still be found in reasonable numbers is Argentina and New Zealand.

ANGUS, HEREFORD and SUSSEX

Due to the fact that these breeds have developed in a similar environment and have been selected for similar production traits allow their discussion as a group. The smaller frame animals are sexually and physiologically early maturing and potentially very fertile – the Angus, in particular, is recognised as being potentially highly fertile. They will combine well with the Sanga and African Zebu in increasing veld productivity in less demanding environments such as the South African Highveld. Such a genotype will have sufficient adaptation and parasite/disease resistance in order to maximise fertility (two-year calving and high reconception rate) on veld plus good rumen stimulating supplement. There will be no need for crop residues, hay, high energy production feed, irrigated pasture, etc. There may be a place for some blood from these breeds in more trying environments, but the composition will have to be much less. They can best be incorporated into the appropriate combinations by using the composites such as Brangus and Braford.

PHOTO 8.15*: An extremely masculine and efficient grass converting Angus bull. He is from a herd where the breeder never selected for large frame. This is the type of bull required in many environments. Genes from such a bull would be an asset, even in some tropical environments, where a small percentage could be combined with other adapted breeds.*

DUAL PURPOSE BREEDS

These are essentially beef breeds with more milk than the average beef breed. As such, and due to the fact that they are larger, they require better nutrition in order to maintain acceptable fertility. The most popular of these breeds is the Simmental, Gelbvieh, South Devon, Braunvieh and Pinzgauer. Although there is individually much variation, all these breeds can collectively be described as being large frame, with above average milk and muscling. It is doubtful whether they have any role to play in improving veld productivity other than the early maturing types used in combination with the African Zebu and Sanga.

CONTINENTAL BREEDS

This is collectively the group of cattle with the largest frame and best meat: bone ratio. The majority of these breeds originate in France and Italy. Included in this group are the Limousin, Charolais, Chianina, Romagnola, Marchigiana and Piedmontese. There may be certain niche markets where these animals can play a role, but in terms of maximising profit/ha on a sustainable basis on veld they are of very limited value. An interesting anomaly amongst the continental breeds is the Aubrac which is smaller frame and was developed under conditions of poorer nutrition.

PHOTO 8.16*: This Aubrac bull photographed (Courtesy of Paul Butler) in the north-western USA is a good example of the type of Continental Breed animal that can be used fruitfully as a purebred on temperate high "octane" grazing or as a crossbred (composite) in other environments. Similar to the Angus in the previous photo, this animal epitomises grass conversion efficiency (full package).*

BREEDING SYSTEMS

Breeding systems refers to the various ways in which a genotype or genotypes can be optimised in terms of complementarity and hybrid vigour in order to attain maximum sustainable profit/ha. This does not refer to within-herd selection but to whether genotype combinations should be made and how to make them.

CONVENTIONAL PUREBREEDING

Conventional purebreeding, where the unique adaptive and productive traits of a genotype are preserved (and improved upon), is essential. But, in order to promote a goal of **maximum sustainable profit/ha** things will have to be done very differently. Selection will have to occur in an environment conducive to identifying the appropriate genotype and not allowing animals to achieve an unnatural genetic potential as is done in stud breeding. The possibility should be considered that an extremely adverse environment (eg. no tick control in a high tick population environment) may induce favourable mutations allowing a population to survive. How else does one explain the fact that European breeds have, through natural selection and in a short period of time, become more heat tolerant (eg. Senepol, Romosinuano) or more tick resistant (Australian Adaptaur) than some of their Bos Indicus counterparts? Surely the genetic variation in the original populations cannot account for such a dramatic change. Is it too far-fetched to consider that environmental stimuli can change the genotype (mutations) on both the macro and micro levels?

Although hybrid vigour is considered to result in greater productivity, this is not necessarily so as shown by results from Matopos, Zimbabwe (Ward,H.K and Dlodlo,S. : The Beef Production Manual of 1987, published by the Cattle Producers Association of Zimbabwe). Of all the different genotypes generated from several purebreds as well as their crossbreds the purebred Mashona was the most productive. Weaner production/500kg of cow (Livestock Unit) bulled was 186. Amongst the closest rivals were Mashona/Afrikaner (173), Nkone/Afrikaner (171) and Brahman/Afrikaner (177) - interestingly, the reciprocal Afrikaner crosses (Afrikaner bull on Mashona, Nkone and Brahman cows) were not as productive. The greater productivity was due more to complementarity (combination of productive and adaptive traits) and less to hybrid vigour.

CONVENTIONAL CROSSBREEDING

Rotational crossbreeding and terminal crossing have several disadvantages. Firstly, purebred bulls of some breeds have trouble surviving in harsh environments. This certainly affects their ability to breed. Secondly, there is a great deal of variation between generations in terms of overall adaptation depending on sire genotype. Another disadvantage relates to the management of more herds (depending on the number of breeds used) during the breeding season. The use of the appropriate crossbred bulls, instead of purebred bulls, is the obvious solution.

CROSSBREEDING OF CROSSBREDS

This refers to the use of crossbred bulls on crossbred cows which allows much greater creativity in terms of hybrid vigour and, in particular, complementarity. In the latter case it allows the use of both adapted bulls and cows. If hybrid vigour is dependent on heterozygosity then this can also be increased by using crossbred bulls (at least four different breeds combined in a single cross). For example, consider the following two options in the high altitude, seasonally wet (long dry season), tropics of Central Africa.

Option 1 is a rotational crossbreeding system using purebred Brahman and Simmental bulls. Although the Brahman/Simmental is considered a good cross a definite problem will arise in terms of adaptation when using Simmental bulls (unadapted) as well as the resultant progeny (from Simmental backcross) containing a majority of European blood. They lack climatic and nutritional adaptation in addition to parasite/disease resistance.

Option 2 is a rotational crossbreeding system using Boran/Mashona and Angoni/Tuli bulls. In all cases bulls, cows and progeny are well adapted. Complementarity is very high (polled, easy care cattle with a good meat: bone ratio and extremely good adaptation) with some hybrid vigour. Although Option 1 probably exhibits a higher degree of hybrid vigour (an important consideration in conventional crossbreeding systems) the veld productivity resulting from Option 2 is much greater.

I believe the so-called advantages of hybrid vigour are overrated with much of the benefits of crossbreeding attributed to hybrid vigour being the result of complementarity (combining adaptive and productive traits). The Matopos Crossbreeding Project (quoted earlier) provides many examples to support this thinking.

The most productive genotype, including crossbreds, in the Matopos Project was the purebred Mashona (186kg of weaner production/500kg cow weight). The Charolais/Mashona crossbred cows, with the theoretical benefits of hybrid vigour, were far less productive (155kg/500kg cow). Even the Mashona/Afrikaner cross (173kg/500kg cow), with theoretically less hybrid vigour, was much more productive than the Charolais/Mashona. These results can only point to the overriding importance of adaptation and complementarity in adverse environments. This can best be achieved by using the appropriate crossbred bulls and crossbred cows.

There is a definite need, and a growing demand, for appropriately bred crossbred bulls. This affords stud breeders a tremendous opportunity to access a much greater market. For example, a Bonsmara breeder could use a percentage of his cows to breed purebred heifers as herd replacements and high quality purebred bulls for sale. The remaining females can be bred to Boran and Nguni bulls in order to produce crossbred bulls for sale to commercial breeders. The crossbred females can be *inter se* mated to produce a Bonsmara/Nguni/Boran cross. With a little promotion such animals will find a ready market and realise very good prices.

PUREBREEDING OF CROSSBREDS

In the previous breeding system two extremely important steps were taken. The first was to identify, in broad terms, the appropriate breeds (genotypes) for a certain environment in relation to complementarity and adaptation as it affects a goal of maximum sustainable profit/ha. The second step was to identify the best bulls within each genotype. There is tremendous variation in all breeds/herds. The third step, which leads to the creation of a new genotype/breed, is when the decision is made to close a herd and select from within – in other words the purebreeding of crossbreds.

There is one important condition in taking this final step. Although the assumption is that the appropriate combinations have been made one must leave room for human error and keep the option open of introducing another genotype at any time in the future. For example, the Boran/Mashona/Angoni/Tuli combination given as the ideal combination for the Central African tropics may be found to be susceptible to trypanosomiasis, a disease transmitted by the tsetse fly. In such a situation an infusion of N'Dama blood (trypanatolerant Bos Taurus breed from West Africa) can solve the problem. The resultant composite would probably need to be no less than 50% N'Dama in order to achieve sufficient disease resistance.

Many current breeds have a problem in that they cannot deliver what they promise to deliver. A good example is the Bonsmara. At the outset Prof. Bonsma stated that the idea in developing the Bonsmara was to breed an animal that would be productive under the sub-tropical veld conditions of the northern regions of South Africa. By implication this would mean climatic adaptation, nutritional adaptation (fat reserves for a long dry season) and parasite/disease resistance. Although there is much variation on an individual basis there can be no doubt that as far as tick resistance (and tick-borne disease resistance) is concerned the Bonsmara breed falls far short of the mark.

A further point to bear in mind is that amongst the conventional composites found in South Africa (Bonsmara, Beefmaster, Brangus, Simbra, Santa Gertrudis) there is little to choose in regard to productivity (See the official performance figures supplied by the ARC). In terms of veld productivity, there is absolutely nothing that makes the Bonsmara stand out. The question that needs to be asked is: Why is this so? The Bonsmara is promoted as a "scientifically bred" breed yet it is no more productive than the other conventional composites found in South Africa and considerably less adapted and veld productive than an "unimproved" breed such as the Nguni and its crosses. What has been said about the Bonsmara, in terms of not delivering what is promised, can be said of the South African Beefmaster (personal experience), Brangus, Santa Gertrudis and Simbra as well.

The above synopsis of some breeds is solely to prove a point. Breeds in general fall far short of what they are made out to be. Within the Bonsmara breed there are undoubtedly animals that are highly productive under commercial ranching conditions. But, there is no doubt that a very large percentage, if not all, of these animals would be highly susceptible to ticks and tick-borne diseases in tropical and sub-tropical regions. What can Bonsmara breeders do about this? Either they admit that their breed has limitations and do something to rectify it or they ignore the facts and live a lie. If indeed they decide to do something, one option is to actively select for tick and disease resistance. This will take considerable time. The other option is to cross with a suitable African breed (or breeds). This cross will automatically have a high degree of resistance which can be further increased through selection. Although the latter option is far more effective and can result in a highly productive genotype through complementing the production attributes of the Bonsmara and the hardiness of another breed (or breeds) it is unlikely to be contemplated by the Breed Society. This, however, does not prevent individual breeders from doing so. The resultant genotype could not be referred to as a

Bonsmara, but it would be far more veld productive, particularly if more appropriate selection criteria were to be used (See Chapter 9: SELECTING FOR FERTILITY). What applies to the Bonsmara, as in this example, applies to any other breed in a similar situation.

It is an indictment against conventional stud breeding when an obvious solution to a major problem is disregarded. But, then again, stud breeding is more about people than cattle. The current state of affairs affords individual breeders with an entrepreneurial spirit a great opportunity. However, it will be a long time before the mainstream breeders catch up with reality.

MATCHING GENOTYPE TO ENVIRONMENT

It needs repeating that there is no universally superior genotype. As previously mentioned, the difference in productivity can be as much as $50 - 100\%$. The environmental factors having the greatest effect on an animal's wellbeing and productivity are climate, nutritional status of the grazing and the incidence of parasites/diseases.

There is obviously variation on a breed basis with regard to overall adaptation and productivity, but there is also a tremendous amount of variation within breeds. Generally speaking breeds can be grouped in terms of nutritional adaptation (relative intake, fat reserves), climatic adaptation (coat type, pigment), resistance to parasites and certain diseases as well as productivity (milk, hormonal balance, meat: bone ratio). However, it is essential that the bulls with the best attributes within a grouping be identified and used for breeding regardless of breed which, in reality, is defined on arbitrary lines. For instance, if the conventional composites are to be used in a breeding system then the best available bulls need to be identified on individual merit whether they are Bonsmara, Beefmaster, Brangus, Simbra, Santa Gertrudis, Droughtmaster or whatever. The same applies to the Zebus, Sangas, Tropically Adapted Bos Taurus, British Breeds, Dual Purpose Breeds and the Continental Breeds.

What follows is an attempt to match genotypes, generated by crossbreeding of crossbreds or purebreeding of crossbreds to certain environments. Examples of the appropriate genotypes are given as a guideline. Breeders must be creative in the breed combinations they make and selective in the bulls they use. These breeding systems, at least initially, are dependent on the use of appropriately selected purebreds.

HUMID, SEASONAL RAINFALL TROPICS

This refers to the high rainfall regions of Zambia, Mozambique and North Zimbabwe. This is one of the most challenging environments for cattle production. The incidence of ticks, blood-sucking insects, internal parasites and diseases is very high. The short, intense rainy season (750 – 1500mm concentrated in 4 months) and long dry season result in poor quality grazing necessitating a nutritionally adapted genotype. Solar radiation in general, and ultraviolet radiation on the central plateau, is very high. The relatively high seasonal humidity, high solar radiation, a relatively small photoperiodic effect and fibrous grass with a high heat increment create a unique challenge in terms of heat adaptation.

PHOTO 8.17 shows low "octane" grass and PHOTO 8.18 shows small frame cows adapted to poor nutrition. The taller the grass the shorter the cattle need to be. The Angoni cows pictured above, and in excellent body condition during the dry season of the seasonal rainfall tropics, weaned Beefmaster-cross calves 80% of their own weight.

Also included in this environment are the wet, seasonal (4 to 8 months) rainfall tropics of northern Australia and Latin America. Although the disease incidence is less than in Africa the climatic and nutritional challenges are similar or greater. The problem in Brazil, for example, of mono-culture pastures and extremely wet conditions resulting in poor nutrition is exacerbated by the use extremely late maturing Zebus. Crossbreeding with European breeds such as the Angus, Limousin and Simmental is clearly not the answer as these crosses are neither nutritionally nor climatically adapted.

Considering the challenges of this environment and the results of the Matopos (Zimbabwe) Crossbreeding Trials (African and Asian breeds and crosses most productive), the Sanga and Zebu breeds should be the sole, or dominant, genotypes used. The Tropically Adapted Bos Taurus and Conventional Composites may play a role under certain conditions if the right selections are made.

BORAN/MASHONA/ANGONI/TULI

All four breeds are climatically adapted with a high, to very high, degree of parasite and disease resistance. Nutritional adaptation/fattening ability and drought tolerance are extremely high in the Boran and Angoni and high in the Mashona and Tuli. The Mashona and Tuli excel in terms of early sexual maturity. Milk production and meat: bone ratio is high in the Boran and Tuli and moderate in the Mashona and Angoni. In addition, the Mashona and Tuli (and some Boran and Angonis) are polled resulting in all animals being polled (inheritance of the polled factor is dominant). Meat quality and dressing percentage will be very high.

I believe there is no better genotype for this cattle "unfriendly" environment. I also believe this environment to be the last frontier for beef production in the world. Here is a great opportunity for breeders with an entrepreneurial spirit. By breeding a Super Zebu (Afrizebu) consisting of African Zebu ecotypes (Boran and Angoni) and a Super Sanga (Afrisanga) consisting of African Sanga ecotypes (Mashona, Tuli, Nguni, Tonga, etc.) all that remains for breeders in the humid tropics is to combine these two genotypes.

SEMI-HUMID, SEASONAL RAINFALL TROPICS AND SUB-TROPICS

This region is represented by South Zimbabwe, the north-eastern part of South Africa down to Zululand, large parts of southern Mozambique and north-eastern Botswana. This environment is, from a nutritional point of view, less challenging than the humid, seasonal rainfall tropics. Rainfall is less (400 – 600mm) resulting in more nutritious veld (also dependent on soil type). Rainfall is also more variable with frequent seasonal and long term droughts. Temperatures are generally high but humidity relatively low except along the east coast. The incidence of ticks and tick-borne diseases is high.

The greatest challenges are high temperatures, ticks and tick-borne diseases and drought. Genotypes need to be adapted to a hot environment, resistant to ticks and the diseases they transmit in addition to being able to fatten quickly and maintain body condition. The appropriate breed groups are the Zebus, Sangas, Tropically Adapted Bos Taurus and Conventional Composites.

MASHONA/BORAN X TULI/BRAHMAN

All four breeds are adapted to a hot environment and resistant to ticks and tick-borne diseases. The Mashona and Tuli are polled and confer early sexual maturity. Milk production is high in all breeds. Muscling is moderate in the Mashona and high in the other three breeds. The Boran fattens very quickly and with good fattening ability in the other breeds drought tolerance will be high.

BORAN/BONSMARA X BEEFMASTER/TULI

All four breeds are adapted to a hot environment but only the Boran and Tuli can be considered to be resistant to ticks and tick-borne diseases. The Tuli is polled and together with the Beefmaster and Bonsmara sexually early maturing. The fattening ability of the Boran is high and that of the other breeds is moderate. All breeds have good milk and a good meat: bone ratio. Overall adaptation and drought tolerance are good, and depending on the specific conditions, tick and disease resistance may be sufficient.

DRY, HOT SUMMERS; WARM WINTER DAYS WITH COLD NIGHTS

This is represented by most of Namibia and Botswana together with the north-western part of South Africa. It includes the Kalahari region of Botswana, Namibia and South Africa. This is an arid, seasonal rainfall (250 – 500mm) area with low humidity throughout the year. Seasonal droughts as well as long term droughts are a feature of this environment requiring genotypes with drought tolerance (fat reserves). Frost is generally severe. The nutritional status of the veld is good although the palatability of grass species varies a great deal. There is a lower incidence of parasites, including ticks and tick-borne diseases. Generally speaking this is a very healthy and forgiving environment for cattle. Although day temperatures can be high, the low humidity and cool nights have an ameliorating effect allowing the European breeds to survive and be relatively productive.

*PHOTOS **8.19** and **8.20** depict high "octane" grass and illustrate the resultant body condition and size of cattle grazing this nutritional grass. Compare this situation to that shown in Photos 18.17 and 18.18. A dry environment with cool nights and high "octane" grass is very forgiving in terms of genotype.*

A wide range of breeds can survive and perform to an acceptable degree in this environment but the appropriate genotype needs to be able to fatten easily and maintain body condition in order to survive drought. The most prominent breed groups will be the Zebu and Sanga. However, the Tropically Adapted Bos Taurus, Conventional Composite and even the European group of breeds can be used if the early maturing types are selected.

BORAN/TULI X AFRIKANER/NGUNI

The Boran has excellent fattening ability which is complemented by the good fattening ability of the other three breeds. The Tuli and Nguni confer early sexual maturity and the Tuli the polled factor. All four breeds have sufficient milk and a good meat: bone ratio. Climatic adaptation and resistance to ticks and tick-borne diseases is high.

BORAN/ANGUS X NGUNI/SIMMENTAL

The Boran together with an early maturing Angus and Nguni will result in a high degree of fattening ability and drought tolerance. The Nguni, Angus and Simmental are sexually early maturing. The Boran, Angus and Simmental will provide sufficient milk and a good meat: bone ratio in the progeny. The Nguni and Boran are the source of resistance to ticks and tick-borne diseases.

BORAN/BONSMARA X NGUNI/SIMBRA

The Nguni and Bonsmara are essential in providing a sufficient degree of early sexual maturity to this combination. The Boran is necessary for fattening ability. The Bonsmara and Simbra, in particular, provide more milk for heavier weaners if this was a specific requirement (Too much milk in the cow can result in an imbalance between nutritional requirement and availability from the veld). The Boran, Bonsmara and Simbra will improve the meat: bone ratio of the Nguni. The Boran and Nguni should provide sufficient resistance to ticks and tick-borne diseases for this specific environment. Climatic adaptation is provided by all four breeds.

COOL, WET SUMMERS; COLD WINTERS

The eastern Highveld of South Africa falls in this environmental category. Summers are wet and cool. Winters are very cold and relatively moist with occasional snow. Summer temperatures do not result in heat stress for all the common breeds. Frost is very severe. Ticks do not generally do physical damage but are a source of tick-borne diseases which can cause serious losses amongst cattle with a low degree of genetic resistance. Summer veld is generally of a high quality but winter (frosted) veld is of low quality and cattle require a high degree of inherent body condition.

The cold winters result in greater stress than summer temperatures. Woolly winter coats (photoperiodic effect is strong enough to allow European and Conventional Composite breeds to grow a winter coat) will aid in reducing energy expenditure and in keeping warm during winter. However, the greatest asset to overwintering in this environment is body fat reserves. This is clearly illustrated by the smooth coated Boran being able to survive low temperatures in dry conditions. The Boran and Nguni are an essential requirement in terms of climatic and nutritional adaptation and disease resistance. Most other breeds can be used in combination with them.

BORAN/NGUNI X BONSMARA/NGUNI

The Nguni is a necessity in this environment in respect of disease resistance, hardiness (nutritional adaptation and climatic stress) and early sexual maturity. The

Boran provides additional winter hardiness (fat reserves) and disease resistance. Both the Bonsmara and Boran have a good meat: bone ratio as well as milk.

BORAN/TULI X NGUNI/BRANGUS

The addition of the Tuli and Brangus to the Boran and Nguni includes the easy-care polled factor without losing too much of the hardiness of the previous combination (50% Nguni). They also add more milk and a better meat: bone ratio. A high degree of early sexual maturity is provided by the Tuli and Nguni.

NORTH AMERICAN RANCHLAND: HOT, HUMID SUMMERS; COLD WINTERS

This refers to the south-eastern United States where the summers are "tropical" and the winters "temperate". Soils are generally infertile and the grazing has a low "octane" rating. Internal and external parasites are prevalent. Cattle need to be nutritionally adapted (small frame), disease/parasite resistant, heat tolerant (smooth summer coat) and cold tolerant (fat reserves). Although the higher latitude (outside the tropics) aids smooth summer coats and woollier winter coats a genetically smooth coat is advantageous. In order to attain maximum sustainable profit/ha any genotype must have a predominance of African breed blood. The reason is that these breeds excel in nutritional adaptation as well as parasite/disease resistance.

BORAN/TULI X MASHONA/BRANGUS

This genotype will be polled, parasite/disease resistant, climatically and nutritionally adapted. Meat: bone ratio will be very high. Meat quality will also be very high.

NORTH AMERICAN RANCHLAND: HOT, DRY SUMMERS; VERY COLD WINTERS

This area is represented by the western United States prairies. Humidity is low, but winter and summer temperatures are extreme. Soils are generally fertile (higher pH) and the "octane" rating of grazing high. Although the "octane" rating of grass is generally high, allowing larger genotypes to be "productive", the earlier maturing (smaller frame) genotypes will show better nutritional adaptation (drought and winter tolerance). This is essential for the attainment of maximum sustainable profit/ha where low inputs and lower selectivity of grazing are requirements. Cattle need to be nutritionally adapted (high relative intake) with the ability to survive cold winters (fat reserves; woolly winter coat). The appropriate genotype will be based on early maturing European breeds. Other breeds with unique attributes (fat reserves) can contribute positively to achieving a goal of maximum sustainable profit/ha.

ANGUS/LASATER BEEFMASTER X GALLOWAY/AUBRAC

The early maturing, hormonally balanced (small frame) Angus is a very productive animal for this environment. The Lasater Beefmaster is unique in the sense that it has a long history of selection for productivity (survival of the fittest) in a seasonally hot and cold environment (Colorado). The Galloway (originally from Scotland) is adapted to cold (woolly winter coat) and poor nutrition (fattens readily). The Aubrac, a French breed, is also unique in the sense that it has a history of production on poor grazing in cold country (much smaller frame than the typical Continental breeds) resulting in the ability to fatten quickly. They have an excellent meat: bone ratio which is also evident in the other three breeds.

3/4 ANGUS 1/4 DRAKENSBERGER X 3/4 AUBRAC 1/4 MASHONA

The above example which could result in a composite of ¾ European and ¼ African breeding is given as an example of how creative modern breeders can be and the potential productivity that could result from optimally combining complementarity (productive and adaptive traits without any antagonisms) with hybrid vigour (British, Continental, Zebu and Sanga breeds). The ¾ European breed blood is essential for adaptation to cold; the ¼ African breed blood adds to hybrid vigour and enhances nutritional adaptation (inherent body condition). Appropriate selection of parent breeding material is essential.

9. SELECTING FOR PROFIT

Whatever breeding system is employed for herd improvement, whether it is conventional purebreeding or purebreeding of crossbreds, within-herd selection is necessary. With a goal of **maximum sustainable profit/ha** appropriate selection criteria need to be used. Absolute measures of performance such as weaning weight, 12 month weight, 18 month weight, weight per day of age, ADG and FCE do not result in more efficient veld convertors but in cattle requiring more external inputs (feed, dip and de-worming drenches) in order to be "productive".

The current measures of fertility such as pregnancy (non-pregnant culled), scrotum circumference, ICP and calving tempo are poorly discerning in terms of the genetic variation of the components of practical fertility (hormonal balance **and** body condition). The result is that fertility is erroneously considered to be lowly heritable (said to be 90% feeding and 10% breeding) with little progress possible through selection.

It is unfortunate, but understandable, that many individuals with questioning minds come to the wrong conclusion regarding the role of genetics in determining veld productivity in general and fertility in particular. Stan Parsons, for instance, talks about "the futility of genetics" in his book: *If You Want to Be a Cowboy Get a Job*. These wrong conclusions stem from the antics of show judges and breed inspectors as well as the negative results of "scientific breeding methods". This does not mean that breeding *per se* is a futile exercise or that fertility is solely dependent on nutrition. It means that inappropriate selection criteria are used and that flawed breeding practices are followed. Those who doubt the value of genetics should consider why certain breeds (genotypes) are more fertile than others when run under the same conditions (Matopos, Zimbabwe and Omatjene, Namibia). They should also consider why there is a 50% - 100% difference in the productive efficiency between breeds (Matopos, Zimbabwe and Belmont Research Station, Rockhampton, Australia).

We have defined the most profitable beef animal (See Chapter 7: THE MOST PROFITABLE BEEF ANIMAL). We now need to "read" (measure, observe) what nature is indicating (body condition, milk, hormonal balance, conformation) to be the most profitable (veld conversion efficiency) animal. To this end there are certain selection procedures that need to be followed.

COW EFFICIENCY

Strictly speaking, and without considering the bigger picture, cow efficiency (calf weight/kg grass consumed) can be measured as calf weight/cow metabolic weight (kg/kg 0.75). In reality, though, there is much more to consider. The cow weight to be used can have a large effect on the figure. For example, a cow with too much milk (relative to the nutritional status of the veld) and in poor body condition will give an inflated figure resulting in an antagonism between cow efficiency and fertility (body condition). Similarly, the sire can influence the size of the calf regardless of the dam's efficiency. The other important consideration is that two heifers with dam's of equal efficiency at weaning, but who differ in size, will have different maturity rates (and required growth rates) influencing their chances of conceiving at 14/15 months. A far more appropriate measure that relates to cow efficiency in the broad sense is calf maturity at weaning.

CALF MATURITY

Calf maturity is calculated some time before a calf is weaned. It is influenced by both the milk yield of the dam and the calf's mature size. The greatest value of this measurement is assessing cow milk yield as well as efficiency in the broader sense. The optimum in terms of cow and calf efficiency is a 40 - 50% maturity at weaning. This puts a ceiling on milk production, which can be excessive relative to nutrition, but allows sufficient maternal influence for a heifer to reach 60% maturity at 12 months – a requirement for conception at 14/15 months.

6 MONTH MATURITY

It is preferable to calculate calf maturity at 6 months rather than at a later age due to the influence of pregnancy status on lactation length. This is particularly true with an extended calving season (2 – 3 months) where certain cows can conceive 1 month after calving and others 3 months after calving. Maturity is calculated using the corrected weight (calf age, dam age, calf sex, calving date) at 6 months relative to the calf's predicted mature size calculated from hip height measurements (See Appendix 1: PREDICTION OF MATURE SIZE IN BULLS FROM HIP HEIGHT MEASUREMENT and Appendix 2: PREDICTION OF MATURE SIZE IN HEIFERS FROM HIP HEIGHT MEASUREMENT). This can be expressed as a percentage or, more appropriately, in the form of a ranked 6 Month Maturity Score.

GRASS CONVERSION EFFICIENCY

It is clear that Feed Conversion Efficiency (FCE) measured as feed/kg gain is mathematically flawed and correlated to poor body condition (See Chapter 6: MEANWHILE, BACK AT THE RANCH............). This applies to both a feedlot test and a veld test (grass intake can be predicted by using a marker such as chromic oxide). The reason for this is that the energy content of live weight gain is not taken into consideration (animals of similar age but different maturity rate are at different levels of fatness resulting in different energy requirements for 1kg gain – fat meat has a higher energy content than lean meat). Neither is the fact considered that such a test is done over a very short period of an animal's life that has little bearing on the bigger picture.

When looking at animals of different size it is apparent that they have to grow in proportion to their size in order to be equally efficient (See Chapter 6: MEANWHILE, BACK AT THE RANCH............). Stated differently, the animal that grows fastest relative to its size is the most efficient. Such an animal will also have the best body condition. It will also have the highest relative intake resulting in it being the most efficient and fattest. Some measure of body condition or relative growth will identify the most efficient animal.

BODY CONDITION

In the absence of meaningful data, body condition/fullness of body (the 8-in-5 package vs. the 9-in-10 package) is the best indicator of growth efficiency. This is a relatively easy matter when it involves the selection of one bull amongst a large group of bulls. But, when it comes to visually ranking all the bulls in a large group the task becomes impossible. Nevertheless, a visual assessment where one or two bulls are selected can be done much more accurately than using growth or FCE figures.

YEARLING MATURITY

Yearling maturity is the most accurate measure of an individual's growth efficiency. It also allows the ranking of a contemporary group of animals from the most efficient to the least efficient as determined by relative intake and reflected in body condition.

12 MONTH MATURITY

This figure is calculated within a contemporary (similar age and management) group on the basis of corrected 12 month weight (6 month weight corrected for seasonal effects and age of dam plus actual gain between 6 and 12 months) expressed as a percentage of predicted (from hip height measurement) mature size. A 12 Month Maturity Score based on a ranking can also be calculated which is more meaningful for selection purposes. (See Appendix 1: PREDICTION OF MATURE SIZE IN BULLS FROM HIP HEIGHT MEASUREMENT and Appendix 2: PREDICTION OF MATURE SIZE IN HEIFERS FROM HIP HEIGHT MEASUREMENT).

It is essential to use 12 Month Maturity in bull selection. Other than the obvious importance of selecting for grass conversion efficiency, 12 Month Maturity is also an indicator of inherent body condition which is an essential component of fertility. In heifers it is not an essential selection criterion since maturity rate will be reflected in 14/15 month conception.

COW FERTILITY

A cow's reproductive performance depends on hormonal balance and body condition. Both hormonal balance and body condition are the result of interaction between inheritance and environment. The relative importance of genes in determining the optimum hormonal balance and body condition is dependent on genotype and environment.

At Belmont Research Station in Australia a Belmont Red (similar to the Bonsmara) line was selected solely for 18 month weight whilst a Belmont Adaptaur (originally Hereford x Shorthorn) line was selected solely for tick resistance (John Frisch 1999: Personal Communication). After a 25 year period of selection the calving rate of the Belmont Red line showed a tendency of declining (77 – 76%) and that of the Belmont Adaptaur a dramatic increase (67 – 82%). What this indicates, in the case of the Belmont Adaptaur, is that at the initiation of selection the hormonal balance was such that a high calving rate was possible. Body condition was the limiting factor. This could have been increased in a single year by feeding, dipping and treating for internal parasites. In such a case the conclusion could be that the heritability of fertility is low and entirely dependent on environment. However, in the experiment body condition was increased indirectly by selection for tick resistance (smooth coat and overall adaptation resulting in a higher relative intake).

In this case the conclusion has to be that fertility is highly heritable. In the Belmont Red, inherent body condition was probably sufficient to allow a calving rate higher than 77% (at initiation of selection). The limiting factor in this case was in all probability hormonal balance. Selecting for scrotal circumference/100kg live weight in bulls, instead of 18 month weight, would result in a much higher calving rate than the 76% recorded at the end of the experiment. It is interesting to note that the tendency shown for a decline in fertility after 25 years of selecting for size, which increased from 463kg to 537kg, in cows was probably due to the fact that inherent body condition was becoming a limiting factor.

It is very clear that the determinants of fertility are highly heritable. The challenge is to identify selection criteria that are highly discerning in terms of the genetic variation of the determinants of fertility. This will make fertility highly heritable and selection effective.

BODY CONDITION AND HORMONAL BALANCE

In the cow it is possible to assess historical fertility. For example, an experienced eye can differentiate between the 50 cows in a group of 100 that calved annually from the age of two years and the 50 that calved annually from the age of three. This is due to the effect that sex hormones have on the appearance of an animal (See Chapter 6: MEANWHILE, BACK AT THE RANCH............). But, it is not possible to predict which 50 heifers in a group of 100 will calve at two years of age and which 50 will only calve at the age of three years. In order to select effectively we need to be able to identify the individual fertility of each cow.

CORRECTED ICP

The interval between calvings (ICP) is the effect of inheritance (hormonal balance and body condition) and environment (cow age, previous ICP, feeding and date of calving in relation to the rains – all determinants of body condition). In its raw form, ICP largely reflects environmental differences making it a poor measure of inherent fertility. However, if a contemporary group of cows (second calvers) that have run in the same herd under the same nutritional status and whose ICP figures have been corrected for date of calving is used then this Corrected ICP will largely reflect genetic (hormonal balance and body condition) differences between animals. It then becomes possible to rank cows from the most fertile to the least fertile and calculate a Fertility Score even though, on the surface, each has an identical calving rate (See Appendix 3: FERTILITY SCORING OF COWS).

CORRECTED PPAP

In cases where cows calve in very good condition (in the middle of the rains in seasonal rainfall environments) they can start cycling 20 days after calving and if bred can conceive to give a very short ICP of approximately 305 days. When the breeding/calving season is planned to coincide with maximum body condition at calving and is restricted to 42 days a very high percentage of suckling cows (80 – 90%) will be cycling before the start of the breeding season. Such a situation, although advantageous, disqualifies the use of CORRECTED ICP since many cows will have cycled several times before breeding resulting in a longer actual ICP to that possible if they were bred earlier.

In lieu of CORRECTED ICP one requires CORRECTED PPAP (post partum anoestrous period or days from calving to first heat cycle). This is calculated in the same way as CORRECTED ICP except that the cows' are checked for heat after calving in order to record individual anoestrous period (PPAP) with this being corrected for influence of date of calving. On this basis cows can be ranked and scored in terms of fertility similar to using ICP. In well managed herds PPAP will become more important than ICP.

If it is not feasible to record PPAP then the alternative would be to extend the second breeding season by introducing bulls immediately after the first calving commences until the end of the breeding season and calculate fertility ranking on the basis of ICP. The subsequent breeding seasons can commence as normal.

BULL FERTILITY

Considered from a narrow perspective, bull fertility (ability to serve and impregnate) is largely dependent on overall adaptation, good hormonal balance and a lack of physical defects hindering serving ability. In contrast to the cow, body condition is of little importance. However, when looking at the bigger picture body condition is vital since a bull's inherent body condition will have a very big influence on his female progeny's practical fertility.

This is one of the big shortcomings in current selection practices where good body condition in the bull is either ignored or discriminated against. Many breeders, particularly in the Bonsmara breed, are aware of the importance of a desirable hormonal balance. They select for this and have some very fertile bulls (in hormonal terms), but neglect body condition with the result that many herds have high academic fertility and low practical fertility (cows need very good nutrition for a high reproductive rate). In addition to selecting for a desirable hormonal balance, active selection for inherently good body condition (high degree of relative intake/relative growth/maturity rate) amongst bulls is essential.

A cow that has calved at 2 + 3 years on veld with limited supplementation and with a top Fertility Score for CORRECTED ICP/PPAP must have high inherent body condition and a desirable hormonal balance. If mated to the appropriate bull all her progeny, including males, will have a high inherent fertility. The first step in bull selection is to identify such cows and select young bulls from them.

This step on its own would go a long way to rectifying the current situation of high academic fertility and low practical fertility.

BODY CONDITION

An essential requirement for 2 + 3 year calving in cows is good body condition. This means that cows that are able to achieve this level of reproduction predominantly on veld have inherently good body condition. Bulls, however, need to be selected directly for body condition at a young age.

12 MONTH MATURITY

As seen earlier, body condition is reflected in 12 Month Maturity. From this figure all bulls can be ranked from the earliest maturing (fattest) to the latest maturing (leanest) and scored accordingly. Only bulls with a high 12 Month Maturity Score must be considered as sires for improving fertility (See Appendix 1: PREDICTION OF MATURE SIZE IN BULLS FROM HIP HEIGHT MEASUREMENT).

HORMONAL BALANCE

An adapted bull with a desirable hormonal balance can serve and impregnate much more than the 25 to 30 odd cows conventionally assigned to him. A good example is a Boran/Nguni/Afrikaner bull owned by Manie and Karin Wessels from Frankfort in the Free State province of South Africa. This bull is a "bosbul" (bull bred outside the norms of SA Studbook and its affiliated breed societies) with the unassuming name of Dunlop (in reference to his black and white markings like a Dunlop tyre). In January of 2009 Dunlop appropriated for himself a herd of cows that had calved the previous winter and had been withheld from breeding in order to coincide with calving in mid-summer. However, unable to keep him from the cows he was allowed to do his work. Thirty days after the first calf was born in mid-October 2009 there were 90 live calves on the ground. We need to breed many more bulls (bosbulle) like Dunlop, regardless of SA Studbook's propaganda.

PHOTO 9.1: *Dunlop, the "bosbul" (bush bull/village bull/mongrel), whose services resulted in 90 live calves on the ground in 30 days.*

12 MONTH SCROTAL CIRCUMFERENCE/100KG MATURE SIZE

This can be measured as millimetres/100kg mature size predicted from hip height measurement (See Appendix 1: PREDICTION OF MATURE SIZE IN BULLS FROM HIP HEIGHT MEASUREMENT).

All bulls are given a score based on a ranking with the highest scored bulls considered for selection (In order to be able to do this a 6/8 MONTH SCROTAL CIRCUMFERENCE/100KG MATURE SIZE measurement is also necessary as some bulls will be culled before 12 months of age).

The reason why scrotal size is measured relative to mature size is that there is a positive correlation between mature size and scrotal size that is unrelated to fertility. Although there is a positive relationship between scrotal size measured in this way (particularly at a young age) and early sexual maturity there is no guarantee that the top scoring bull will impregnate the most calves – the ultimate test for bull fertility.

BREEDING ABILITY

The worst scenario in terms of fertility is single siring with a fertile ox in an extended breeding season. The opposite would be multi-siring in a restricted breeding season in order to allow the most capable bull the opportunity to sire the most calves. If such a bull is identified through DNA testing then the bull with the highest libido, the largest volume of high quality semen and the best serving capability is known. He will also have the highest practical fertility if he has inherently good body condition (high 12 month maturity). In practice such a test can be done by breeding the best yearling bulls that have been selected for all the economically important traits, including fertility (fertile dam, high 12 month maturity and large 12 month scrotal circumference/100kg mature size), in a multi-sire herd to yearling heifers. A ratio of 1 bull: 10 heifers should allow a sufficient number of selected bulls to prove their breeding capability under competition during a restricted breeding season.

EASY-CARE

One way in which to increase profit/ha is to reduce inputs. Apart from the obvious one of feed there are costs involved in dipping, dosing for internal parasites as well as labour. There is also the consideration of calving ease, mothering ability, ease of handling and dehorning.

CALVING EASE

One of the most demoralising situations for a rancher to be confronted with is difficult births. This is generally the result of large calves at birth as well as cows/heifers with a restricted birth canal due to a flat and level rump. This is the result of selection by man. All naturally selected cattle (Zebus and Sangas together with the Latin American Criollo breeds) have sloping rumps as viewed from the side and "roofy "rumps as viewed from behind. Such animals have little difficulty calving, even as yearling heifers.

Calving difficulty has become such a problem in some breeds that internal pelvic measurements are taken in order to cull potentially difficult calving heifers before breeding. I understand that such a serious situation requires drastic action and that it may be the less painful option open for some breeders in the short term. But, selecting bulls on the same basis is inviting further problems. A large pelvis is a female trait. The tendency for a large pelvis in bulls will be linked to a hormonal imbalance (low level of testosterone). This way of thinking created a problem (calving difficulty) in the first instance and will create a further problem (bulls and cows with a hormonal imbalance) in the near future.

Is it too difficult for breeders to accept that nature should be the judge of what is desirable or undesirable? The surest way to select for calving ease in a herd is to breed heifers at 14/15 months of age to calve as two-year-olds. This solution, however, is long term and should be followed by breeders of all breeds. The short term solution is to switch to a breed, or breeds, that do not have difficult births. The "unimproved" breeds are the best source.

TICK RESISTANCE

The reliance on the use of dips to keep cattle tick-free has a few certain outcomes. The first one is that we are breeding dip resistant ticks instead of tick resistant cattle. The second one is that we are simplifying the environment (reducing biodiversity) by killing off many beneficial creatures such as oxpeckers (and other birds) and dung beetles. I personally witnessed a case where a rancher applying a small amount (5ml) of a green label pour-on dip (supposedly less toxic) to the tail around the rectal area of cattle poisoned dung beetles for a period of four days afterwards. This was very obvious as we observed the concentrated dung of cows grazing under UltraHigh Density Grazing. Another result is that the acquired immunity of cattle is much lower leaving them more susceptible to tick-borne diseases. The only sustainable solution is the breeding of tick resistant cattle.

In order for selection to be highly effective there first has to be sufficient genetic variation. This can be achieved by using a breed with an already high level of tick resistance, by infusing genes from a different genotype (breed) or by somehow inducing mutations (as probably occurred with the Adaptaur during decades of selection). A further requirement is the use of discerning selection criteria.

12 MONTH MATURITY

In the absence of any form of tick control in an environment with a very large tick population this criterion should be sufficiently discerning in terms of genetic resistance to ticks and tick-borne diseases. This is due to the fact that susceptible individuals will have a lower growth rate. An important proviso is that calves are exposed to a high level of tick infestation at an age where pre-immunity is still high in order to acquire long term immunity to tick-borne diseases and trigger the inherent mechanisms that repel ticks.

TICK COUNTS

Tick counts (number of ticks) or scores (5 = no ticks; 1 = extremely high numbers) can be used where the tick population is high enough to express sufficient variation amongst animals. Where the incidence of ticks is too low and selection for high resistance is necessary (breeder selling bulls to areas with high tick populations) tick counts will have to be done on animals that have been artificially infested. This will require assistance from veterinary labs at universities or similar institutes.

RESISTANCE TO INTERNAL PARASITES

The use of anthelmintics to de-worm livestock has a similar effect as dips in treating ticks. We are simplifying the environment (even greater effect on dung beetles than dips) and breeding poison resistant worms. All the mechanisms behind parasite resistance are not known. What I do know from experience is that cattle in good body condition (effective immune system?) can somehow control/suppress parasites to a level where they are not unduly affected. In my ranching career of 27 years I never routinely dosed my cattle. This was in a high rainfall environment where the recommendation was for routine dosing, particularly for liver fluke.

The only exception I made was when I had to treat very old cows that were down in condition (dry year) and had virtually succumbed to liver fluke. I had a similar experience with tick-borne diseases. Mature animals that were treated infrequently for ticks only developed tick-borne disease when they were down in condition. This experience was with Beefmasters. Better adapted stock (African Zebu and Sanga) will be even more tolerant/resistant and a good starting point for selection.

12 MONTH MATURITY

As in the case of ticks, selection for grass conversion efficiency/body condition/adaptation in the presence of a high internal parasite burden will result in selection for parasite resistance. Any animal adversely affected by parasites will have a poor growth rate resulting in decreased maturity.

FAECAL EGG COUNT

Sampling of the dung in order to determine faecal egg counts is a means of ranking animals relative to resistance. If effective, this measurement should be in broad agreement with 12 Month Maturity in which case the two criteria can be used together for greater discernment.

MOTHERING ABILITY

Cows need an inherently good maternal instinct in order to accept their calves at birth and protect them until they are weaned. This is particularly true of heifers calving at a young age. In terms of selection there is little chance that the progeny of a poor mother will be retained as a bull. However, on a breed basis selection is important. The African Zebu and Sanga cow is generally a very good mother. This must be the result of them having to contend with predators in their recent past.

TEMPERAMENT

No serious rancher likes working with rodeo cattle. Neither are stubborn cattle an asset when a large herd has to pass through the handling kraal. Cattle that habitually leave the herd and go through fences should be culled in lieu of being eaten by predators.

Cattle with a strong herd instinct are much easier to handle particularly when it comes to UltraHigh Density Grazing (electric fencing and physical herding). They also have a tendency to follow other cattle with the result that they flow much easier when being moved through the handling kraal or to the next paddock. But, such cattle are very intelligent and can become unruly if handled badly. They definitely respond negatively to sticks and stones (and nails on the end of sticks as seen in Brazil). The Zebu and Sanga fall in this category. Many of them also show an affinity for man.

When it comes to selection or culling, animals can be identified in terms of their reaction to day to day routines such as being herded and moved constantly to new "paddocks" (UltraHigh Density Grazing). Where this kind of management is not possible they will need to go through a selection process such as done on the

Lasater Ranch. After weaning all calves are subjected to handlers who test their response to close contact (touching or feeding out the hand) in a confined area.

PHOTO 9.2: *African cattle have an affinity for man. Pictured (Courtesy of Antoinette Zietsman Coetzee) is a small herd being swum across the crocodile infested Zambezi River by herdsmen in canoes.*

POLL

Dehorning is performed on most commercial ranches worldwide. Having grown up on such a ranch I came to accept that dehorning is part of ranching without questioning the reasons for such a practice. The major reasons cited for dehorning are ease of handling (better flow through handling facility) and less physical damage to animals (bruising of carcases). The validity of these arguments depends to a large degree on circumstances. The major argument against dehorning is the trauma involved (animal rights movement will become more vocal) as well as the injury that can result (screw worm infestation in humid environments).

A simple solution to the question of whether to dehorn or not is the breeding of polled cattle. Making matters easier is the fact that the polled gene is dominant. The only issue to consider when doing this is prepuce problems in some bulls from certain breeds. Breeds in which prolapse is correlated to the polled factor are mainly of European origin. The main exception is the Tuli. The African breeds in which there is no such correlation are the Mashona and Angoni.

PHOTO 9.3: *Dehorning of cattle is a labour intensive and traumatic exercise. Naturally polled bulls with a tight sheath, as seen in this Romosinuano/European breed composite (Chaco, Paraguay), are an asset.*

CONFORMATION

When assessing conformation the challenge is to distinguish between what is important and what is irrelevant.

FUNCTION

The functional aspects of conformation are very important. They are of greater importance in the bull than in the cow. To be considered are obvious genetic defects, pigmentation of exposed areas, eyes (some polled African breeds have slit or bulging eyes that are prone to opthalmia), sheath in bulls, udder and teats in cows, testes (uniformity, size and consistency), hoofs and legs. Breeders should use discretion in their decisions. It is pathetic to see some of the decisions made by show judges and breed inspectors. The latest discrimination is a twisted scrotum (off-centre attachment of the scrotal ligament). Bulls with otherwise perfect testes are being culled in the name of science when scientific investigation found no relationship between scrotal twist and fertility. It is also evident that nature tolerates much more variation in angle of the leg, for instance, than man. With man it is usually a case of making the unimportant important and the important unimportant.

MEAT: BONE RATIO

What is important in terms of conformation is meat: bone ratio which has a positive influence on carcase dressing percentage. A 5% higher dressing percentage on a 400kg live animal translates into a 20kg heavier carcase. In monetary terms the added value is considerable. This has an important bearing on bull selection. Apart from the increase in carcase value, a good meat: bone ratio in bulls is positively related to early physiological maturity (fatness) as well as early sexual maturity (testosterone and muscling).

10. ACCELERATING NATURAL SELECTION

Genetic change is only positive if it results in survival of the fittest as opposed to survival of the prettiest. This will only occur if nature is the ultimate judge of what is desirable or undesirable. It is imperative that we "read" nature correctly as attempted in the previous section (See Chapter 9: SELECTING FOR PROFIT. The best the breeder can do is to accelerate the process of natural selection.

LIMIT THE NUMBER OF TRAITS

The fewer the traits selected for the faster the progress. This means ignoring the unimportant and concentrating on the important. The important are, in broad terms, grass conversion efficiency, hormonal balance, optimum milk, easy-care and functional conformation. The specific selection criteria can, in most circumstances, be limited to 12 Month Maturity, 6 Month Maturity, Corrected ICP/PPAP, Bull Serving Ability and Meat: Bone Ratio.

ELIMINATE NEGATIVE CORRELATIONS

Where is the logic in selecting for ADG/FCR (leanness) and Scrotal Size (hormonal balance) when practical fertility is determined by hormonal balance **and** good body condition. Evidence of such an antagonism is the fact that female progeny of Gold Merit bulls are definitely no more fertile than female progeny of Sub-Merit bulls (Bonsmara 2007). In fact, the contrary appears to be true (19 day shorter ICP for daughters of Sub-Merit bulls as opposed to those of Gold Merit bulls). Effective selection results from non-antagonistic selection criteria being used.

MEASURABLE GENETIC VARIATION

Selection is not possible unless there is genetic variation between animals that can be seen or measured. If this is not so, steps need to be taken to create measurable/observable variation.

INFUSION

In a situation where there is no, or very little, genetic variation the required genes have to be introduced from an outside source. If, for instance, a breeder decided that he needed the polled factor in his cattle he could introduce the genes from one of the polled breeds, bearing in mind that some polled cattle in certain breeds carry the genes for prepuce problems. A breeder of a conventional composite breed (Beefmaster, Bonsmara, Brangus, Simbra, Santa Gertrudis) in the humid, seasonal rainfall tropics of North Zimbabwe, Zambia, Mozambique and Latin America will realise, contrary to breed society propaganda, there is insufficient climatic and nutritional adaptation as well as parasite/disease resistance for maximum sustainable profit/ha.

The solution would be the formation of a crossbred foundation (eg. Bonsmara/ Sanga/Zebu) allowing the breeding of a veld productive genotype. The only problem with such an approach is that most breeders, for some or other reason, lack the confidence to do so. In such a case they are condemning their herds to sub-optimal productivity. Breed creation (genotype fixation) is not the sole domain of professors and research stations.

Manie and Karin Wessels of Frankfort, in the Free State province of South Africa, (owners of Dunlop) realised several years ago that their Bonsmara cows, some of which were potentially very productive, lacked nutritional adaptation (no crop residues or hay in winter) and tick-borne disease resistance. They opted for the fastest and surest way forward by crossing the Bonsmara with African breeds (predominantly Nguni with some Boran and Tuli), closing their herd and selecting for veld productivity. After only a few years they are in the enviable situation where up to 90% of their heifers conceive at 14/15 months to produce their first calf at two years of age. Up to 80% reconceive to produce their **second** calf at three years of age with breeding restricted to 42 days and nutrition consisting of a good rumen stimulating lick on veld – no crop residue, hay or centre pivots. This is a good example of "organised common sense" (true science) as opposed to "modern breeding methods" (pseudo science/superstition).

ENVIRONMENTAL MANIPULATION

Management or environmental conditions can be such that genetic variation is masked. A case in point is breeding heifers at 27 months of age to calve at three years (common practice). In conventionally managed studs, where nutrition is generally adequate, this allows insufficient selection pressure on nutritional adaptation and early sexual maturity. The solution is to breed all heifers at 14/15 months regardless of weight. It may be that a small percentage will calve at two years and an even smaller percentage will reconceive to produce a second calf at three years. Genetically speaking this is a very good situation because the breeder has identified the genotype that is most fertile (body condition and hormonal balance) under his conditions. This is the female foundation from which bulls can be selected in order to pass on the genes for fertility (body condition and hormonal balance) to the rest of the herd. The heifers that do not conceive at 14/15 months can be bred at a later stage. They do not have to be culled, but they are only relevant in terms of maintaining or expanding herd size.

A further example of unmasking genetic variation would be minimal dipping or no dipping at all (providing animals have acquired immunity to tick-borne diseases) where animals are selected for tick resistance. The same approach would apply in the case of breeding for resistance to internal parasites.

GENETICALLY DISCERNING SELECTION CRITERIA

There is no lowly heritable, economically important trait. Fertility, maturity rate, milk production and meat to bone ratio are all highly heritable traits **if** the appropriate measurements are used.

CONTEMPORARY COMPARISON

In order for comparison between animals to be fair and meaningful it has to be done on a contemporary basis. For example, ICP records for cows of varying age that are run in a single herd are meaningless as an indicator of fertility due to the fact that cow age influences ICP. Mature cows are able to maintain better body condition than young or old cows thus giving them a shorter ICP. A fairer comparison would be amongst cows producing their second calf with the same management history. However, this is still far from ideal if cows calved at different dates relative to the rains resulting in differences in nutrition at calving. These environmental/management differences have to be eliminated by mathematical corrections as shown below.

ENVIRONMENTAL CORRECTION

Cows calving at different dates relative to the rains need to have their ICPs corrected in order to use Corrected ICP as an indicator of genetically determined fertility. By drawing a graph (regression analysis or "best fit" line calculated from the average ICPs at fortnightly or monthly intervals) and comparing individuals in terms of their actual ICP relative to the average at that particular calving date a correction can be made and/or an index calculated (See Appendix 3: FERTILITY SCORING OF COWS).

This Corrected ICP in contemporary groups will largely reflect genetic differences in body condition and hormonal balance and as such will be a fair indicator of genetically determined fertility. In other words the heritability of fertility measured in this way will be high.

HIGH SELECTION DIFFERENTIAL

Selection differential refers, in particular, to the proportion of bulls selected for breeding. The smaller the proportion (percentage) of bulls used for breeding the larger the genetic change. The smaller the proportion of appropriately selected bulls used the greater the improvement. A start can be made in most herds by using one good bull per 50 cows instead of the usual one per 25 cows.

ARTIFICIAL INSEMINATION

A.I. is by far the most cost effective means of effecting genetic change. For the first 7 years of my ranching career I never used a bull. Subsequent to that I used home-bred bulls as well as semen from them. Without A.I. it would have been impossible to make the progress that was achieved. With an appropriate breeding season I was able to inseminate 80% of lactating cows over an 11 day period (one Estrumate injection) resulting in up to 60% of calves being born to A.I. in the first two weeks of the calving season. The degree of genetic change and the effectiveness of selection with A.I. can be tremendous.

The technical aspect of A.I. is relatively easy. The most difficult part is having cows coming on heat and identifying them. The first challenge is overcome with an appropriate calving season (See Chapter 6: MEANWHILE, BACK AT THE RANCH…………). The second challenge is overcome by heat-spotting with teaser bulls and/or the use of some technical aid such as colour-changing stickers on the cow's rump.

EMBRYO TRANSFER

The technique of embryo transfer has theoretically opened access to genetic material across the world. I say theoretically because "important" men sitting behind desks in big buildings still have the final say in issuing import permits.

There is no doubt that embryos have replaced the importation of live animals. Apart from this, the future of embryo transfer lies in identifying the truly superior females, breeding them to truly superior bulls and increasing these genes via A.I. *In vitro* fertilisation of ova will aid the process.

SHORT GENERATION INTERVAL

Assuming the use of appropriate selection criteria, the quicker a generation becomes obsolete the better. This implies breeding young and replacing bulls with their own sons as soon as possible.

BREEDING YOUNG

By breeding bulls and heifers to produce calves at two years instead of the normal three years, generation interval is decreased by approximately 30%. Genetically speaking, change (hopefully progress) is 30% faster. Whatever arguments are raised against early breeding the question that needs answering is: How can a breeder afford not to breed early?

QUICK GENETIC TURNOVER

As soon as a bull produces breeding age (15 months) sons he is obsolete. Either he is being used extensively in the herd via A.I. (passed the breeding ability test through DNA sampling) or he is at the point of being replaced by the younger generation. Either way his services are no longer required. To a lesser extent the same applies to the older generation cows waiting to be replaced by the younger generation. The quicker one generation can be replaced by the next generation the better (assuming appropriate selection).

MUTATIONS

Reference has been made to mutations (See CONVENTIONAL PUREBREEDING) in which tropically adapted Bos Taurus breeds were discussed. One example is the Australian Adaptaur (Hereford/Shorthorn composite) which has been selected for resistance to the Australian Blue Tick to the extent that some animals are completely resistant and confer greater resistance when compared to the progeny of the Belmont Red (similar to the Bonsmara) and Brahman when crossed with these breeds (John Frisch, 1999: Personal Communication). Another case to consider is that of the Latin American breeds of Bos Taurus origin such as the Romosinuano and Senepol that are apparently even more heat resistant than the Brahman (Work done in heat chambers in the USA).

A third example of dramatic genetic change that has occurred is the trypano-tolerance (disease transmitted by the Tsetse Fly) of the West African N'Dama (Bos Taurus). It is inconceivable that there was sufficient genetic variation in the original populations to allow such effective selection. Surely mutations must have occurred. Are all mutations random or are there environmental stimuli triggering desirable (a question of life or death) mutations that can be employed by breeders?

It is clear that environment can change the genotype of a population over time. This is the essence of "survival of the fittest". If this can occur at the macro level it must surely be able to occur at the micro level (mutations) as well. If this is true, and I believe it is highly probable, then breeders need to subject their animals to extreme conditions to trigger desirable mutations. For example, subject test herds to extreme conditions (poor nutrition, no parasite/disease control) and allow only the fittest to survive. The prudence of such an exercise is apparent even in the absence of mutations since any genetic variation there may be can be fully exploited.

11. THE VELDMASTER (AFRICARNE)

Until 1988 I had concentrated on adapting Beefmasters of Lasater origin (upgraded from an Afrikaner-type base using Lasater Beefmaster semen) to tropical sourveld conditions. Although much progress was made in terms of nutritional adaptation (from relatively large frame to medium frame) it became clear that further change was needed in this regard (particularly when grazing non selectively) in addition to much greater tick and disease resistance. It was also clear that the only way to do this within a lifetime was to infuse African breed blood and select from that base.

The first Mashona cross calves were born to Beefmaster cows in 1989 (Superior results were obtained from semen of well muscled Mashona bulls on Beefmaster cows as opposed to the reciprocal cross). As an experiment, none of these calves, together with those from a Beefmaster control, were dipped or treated for internal parasites. Not a single Mashona-cross calf became infested with screw-worm or developed any disease. Half the Beefmaster calves developed sweating sickness (tick-borne pathogen) and coccidiosis (bacterial diarrhoea) with some dying even after treatment. The Mashona-crosses were visibly in better body condition with sleeker, shinier coats. This was the beginning of Veldmaster development in southern Africa (There is currently interest in developing its counterpart, the Africarne, in the Americas) which now has a much broader base than the Beefmaster and Mashona.

The breeding of the Veldmaster, in a broad sense, arose from the need for an animal that is able to perform at maximum fertility (in particular, good body condition) under conditions of Non-Selective Grazing. The currently recognised breeds that come closest to achieving this are the African Sanga and African Zebu. Individually, however, they do have their shortcomings which can be eliminated by combinations amongst them and other breeds. The other consideration in breeding a new genotype is the fact that none of the recognised breeders of any of the African breeds are actively selecting for a high relative intake (indirectly developed in traditional society by kraaling). For many of them colour markings, shape, size and twist of this and that are more important than maturity rate and meat: bone ratio. Veldmaster breeders have, within certain guidelines, freedom to breed cattle that will enable them to achieve maximum sustainable profit/ha under their conditions. With this freedom comes individual responsibility for the product – no formal herd inspection or society sponsored sales.

GOAL

The goal is not to breed the fastest growing cattle, the best feedlot feed convertors, the heaviest weaners or the ideal carcase. Neither is a specific colour important. The goal is **maximum sustainable profit/ha**. What is important is efficient grass conversion (high relative intake), good body condition, a desirable hormonal balance, optimum milk, a high meat: bone ratio and easy-care characteristics.

ORGANISATIONAL GUIDELINES

The problem with cattle breeding organisations is that people become more important than cattle. In such a situation decisions revolve around the interests of people with influence and not around veld productivity. With Veldmaster breeding the focus is on breeding veld productive cattle that, with appropriate veld management, will achieve **maximum sustainable profit/ha**. To this end, all negative human influences must be eliminated.

FRANCHISE

Breeders are individually involved on a franchise basis whereby the Veldmaster name (registered) and brand, together with certain performance symbols, can be used to guarantee a product. The breeder agrees to operate within specified guidelines and pays an annual royalty. The main purpose behind such an arrangement is to have structure behind Veldmaster breeding whilst eliminating negative human behaviour. It is also a means of selecting breeders who agree with the philosophy and are committed to breeding veld productive cattle.

NO FORMAL HERD INSPECTION

If the guidelines are adhered to then the resulting cattle will be a product of natural selection with varying degrees of superiority as signified by the performance symbols. Formal herd inspection would be counter productive and open the way for an expression of egos. Visual assessment is the responsibility of individual breeders.

NO BETWEEN HERD COMPARISONS

There must be no comparison between cattle bred by different breeders. Firstly, this is impossible with traits that are subject to a high degree of genotype x environment interaction. Secondly, it introduces an element of competition driven by ego. It is up to individuals to decide whether another breeder has genetic material that is superior to their own and which can be used to advantage.

USE OF A PREFIX

Not all Veldmasers are the same in the same way that individuals in a family differ. Each herd must be strongly identified with a prefix name.

NO APPROVED SALES

Each breeder has freedom, within certain guidelines, to breed a unique genotype. Each breeder is also solely responsible for his cattle. Individuals are free to have a combined sale. They must, however, be mindful that sale animals will have to run under the same conditions for a considerable time prior to sale in order to prevent some animals acquiring an unfair advantage.

NO COMPETITIVE SHOWING

Breeders can exhibit their cattle for promotional purposes provided it is done without an element of competition.

BREEDING GUIDELINES

The breeding guidelines allow the breeder leeway to breed an animal suited to his conditions starting from a foundation of climatic and nutritional adaptation as well as resistance to parasites and diseases.

BLOOD COMPOSITION

Veldmasters need as much African breed blood as possible (reflecting environmental conditions), but with a minimum of 50% (All such animals are designated Basic Veldmaster and branded V). Inclusion of non-African breeds may be necessary from an environmental point of view (cold winters) in addition to strengthening characteristics that may be lacking (muscling?) in some of the African breeds. It is important to make the appropriate bull choices (8-in-5 packages) from whatever breed.

HIGH SELECTION DIFFERENTIAL

This is essential. Without the use of A.I. it is virtually impossible to combine all the desired traits (muscling, early sexual and physiological maturity, poll, pigment, etc.) in a bull.

BREEDING AT 14/15 MONTHS

All heifers and as many bulls as possible must be bred at the age of 14/15 months. Calving at 2 + 3 years is what differentiates Veldmasters from most other breeds and determines the Standard of Excellence of a Veldmaster.

SELECTION CRITERIA

COW FERTILITY

A Fertility Score (1 – 10) based on a ranking calculated from Corrected ICP/PPAP between the first two calvings indicates an individual cow's fertility relative to its contemporaries and consequently its degree of excellence. Any Veldmaster cow with a 2 + 3 year calving record is designated either Superior Select (branded V/SS) if she falls in the top 50% (Fertility Score of 6 – 10) or Select (branded V/S) if she falls in the bottom 50% (Fertility Score of 1 – 5) as determined by Corrected ICP/PPAP. Those not calving at 2 + 3 years remain with a V brand and remain Basic/Unselected Veldmaster. They can be retained for breeding but only their female progeny can receive a higher designation if they pass the 2 + 3 test.

BULL FERTILITY

All bulls receive their dam's fertility designation and branded V, V/S or V/SS. In addition to this they are also scored for 12 Month Scrotal Circumference/100kg Mature Size as predicted by hip height measurement (See Appendix 1: PREDICTION OF MATUE SIZE IN BULLS FROM HIP HEIGHT MEASUREMENT). A further group of selected bulls are multi-sired at 14/15 months and tested for Serving Ability (proportion of calves sired as determined by DNA tests). The most fertile of these bulls are used for breed improvement via A.I.

COW EFFICIENCY

Cow efficiency is indicated by 6 Month Maturity which is calculated for both heifer and bull calves.

12 MONTH MATURITY

Yearling maturity is a compulsory measurement for all male calves remaining intact at this age. A score is calculated on the basis of the average of all bulls at 12 months relative to the average of all bulls at 6 months. That is, individual ranking/score at 6 and 12 months may differ but the average ranking/score of the remaining bulls at 12 months will reflect their average ranking/score at 6 months.

TICK COUNT

Despite a high degree of resistance being reflected in 12 Month Maturity (in the absence of dipping in tick infested environments) a Tick Count will be the best selection criterion. In environments with a low tick population artificial infestation with laboratory bred larvae will be required to obtain a meaningful Tick Count.

FAECAL EGG COUNT

Resistance to parasites, in the absence of de-worming, will be reflected in 12 Month Maturity. If greater accuracy of genetic resistance is required, Faecal Egg Count or a measure of anaemia as indicated by the colour of the mucous membrane under the eye lid should be considered.

EASY-CARE

- TEMPERAMENT   Veldmasters need to respond positively to good handling. This can be judged at weaning in a similar way as done at the Lasater ranch.

- MOTHERING ABILITY   Some breeds, in particular the zebu, do have a problem mothering their calves when calving at a young age. Sangas are less prone to this problem.

- CALVING EASE   Care must be taken in selecting the parent breeds in forming a Veldmaster base. Breeds or herds without a two year calving history should be avoided as a rule. The more Sanga blood the less chance of calving difficulty. Late maturing, heavy boned animals must be avoided at all costs.

- POLL   The polled factor, without prepuce problems is an asset. However, this should not be acquired at the expense of other functionally important characteristics.

- PIGMENT   All areas exposed to the sun should be pigmented. This applies particularly to the eyes and hoofs (dark hoofs are less prone to foot-rot and hoof growth).

MEAT: BONE RATIO

A high Meat: Bone Ratio is an important attribute required by Veldmasters. It results in a higher carcase value (higher dressing percentage) and is a visual correlation with early maturity (the 8-in-5 package vs. the 9-in-10 package). Well muscled bulls will sell for a premium.

MANAGEMENT GUIDELINES

The management guidelines serve to maximise profit/ha on a sustainable basis in addition to accelerating natural selection.

SHORT BREEDING SEASON

A short breeding season (not longer than 42 days) allows for effective selection, supplementation and A.I. In the initial stages of breeding when A.I. has priority and the breeder is moving towards a single breeding season two or three breeding seasons may be employed in preference to an extended one.

ARTIFICIAL INSEMINATION/EMBRYO TRANSFER

This is essential in order to make progress. There is limited, but important scope, for embryo transfer in herd improvement. Once the desired combination is made through embryo transfer the resulting bulls can accelerate herd improvement via A.I.

EFFECTIVE SUPPLEMENTATION

Effective supplementation refers to maintaining a healthy population of rumen microbes in order to benefit fibre digestion and grass intake. Relatively small amounts (not more than 0.4 % of body weight) of protein (or non-protein nitrogen), readily assimilated energy and certain minerals are usually all that is required.

NO, OR MINIMAL, DIPPING

A major objective of Veldmaster breeding is ecologic sustainability. This means the rancher must eventually be in a situation where no poison (dip) is used. We have breeds that are highly resistant to ticks that can be combined to form a Veldmaster base, but even these animals have to be challenged by ticks in order for the inherent tick repelling mechanisms to work effectively. Therefore, in the worst tick scenario it may be initially (before selection for tick resistance) necessary to have limited artificial tick control. In most instances (with the appropriate breed combinations) no tick control will be necessary if animals have acquired immunity to tick-borne diseases. Problems may arise where animals become stressed (movement to a new environment, poor body condition) or an unfamiliar tick-borne disease is introduced. In such cases blocking with an antibiotic may be required.

NO DOSING

There is no need to dose animals for internal parasites provided the genotype is appropriate. Cattle with a healthy immune system (good body condition) will limit parasite infestation.

GRAZING MANAGEMENT

It is a requirement that all Veldmaster breeders practise appropriate grazing management. This means some form of high impact and Non-Selective Grazing. The breeders practising the highest degree of Non-Selective Grazing will have the edge in promoting their cattle as being veld productive.

PHOTOS 11.1 and **11.2**: *Early maturing and masculine Bar Z Veldmaster bulls.*

PHOTOS 11.3 *and* ***11.4****: Early maturing and feminine Bar Z Veldmaster cows.*

12. PRACTICAL BREEDING SUGGESTIONS

The foregoing, in this part on cattle breeding and management, has been an attempt to debunk conventional stud breeding and "modern breeding" myths. I have also attempted to pave an alternate way with nature as mentor. In the time that I have been writing this book I have also become aware that it is solely experience that creates confidence. Unfortunately, for most of us at least, experience only comes after trial and error over a long period of time. By short-circuiting trial and error (sharing experiences) I have tried to help the reader cut down on the time normally required to attain sufficient confidence in order to make decisions contrary to convention. I further intend helping him understand, in the words of Thomas Huxley, *"that science is nothing but organised common sense"*. To this end I would like to take him on a step-by-step process in breeding beef cattle that will help him achieve **maximum sustainable profit/ha**.

BREED SELECTION

This depends largely on environment and to a lesser extent on breeds readily available. In this age of A.I. and E.T. (embryo transfer) it is theoretically (red tape is still a problem) possible to obtain genetic material from anywhere in the world.

Without any doubt, the most tropically productive cattle are to be found in the African Zebu, African Sanga and African Bos Taurus (N'Dama) groups. This does not mean there aren't individually productive cattle amongst the Asian Zebu and Tropically Adapted Bos Taurus breeds. There are and they can be used in combination with the African breeds in order to eliminate some shortcomings. But, the basis has to be the African breeds. For example, the Red Sindi as found in

172

Brazil is a smaller frame Asian Zebu that can be used in combination with the African breeds in order to improve milk production without losing overall tropical adaptation. It also has a solid red colour (good pigment) and a very good meat: bone ratio. One could use the Senepol to possibly generate hybrid vigour, but the breed did not prove to have any advantage over the Tuli in crossbreeding trials in the USA.

The Conventional Composites such as the Bonsmara, Beefmaster, Brangus, Braford, Simbra and Droughtmaster may be adapted to heat, but they fall far short when it comes to adaptation to conditions of poor nutrition, parasites and disease. The earlier maturing individuals within these breeds can be used in combination with the African breeds. However, under most tropical conditions the African blood would still need to be in the majority.

As far as the other ranching regions of the world are concerned (prairies of North America, South American sub-continent, more temperate regions of Australia and South Africa) I believe the African breeds (particularly the Sanga) still need to be used in order to achieve maximum sustainable profit/ha. The only exception may be the northern USA and Canada where extreme cold could nullify the main advantages of the African breeds – a high relative intake and disease/parasite resistance.

The proportion of African blood required outside the tropics will vary depending on climate and the nutritional status of the grazing. Poor nutrition, parasites/diseases and hot, humid summers will favour African blood which will combine well with the earlier maturing types within the Tropical Bos Taurus, Conventional Composites and British Beef breeds as well as some of the smaller Continental/Dual Purpose breeds such as the Tarentaise and Aubrac. The South African Highveld, for example, is not climatically extreme in terms of heat but requires genotypes with no less than 50% African blood due to poor winter nutrition (in the absence of crop residues) and tick-borne diseases. The North American prairies may benefit from a minimum of 25% African breed blood due to the higher relative intake this may provide.

BREEDING SYSTEM

Following are four options that have a place in sustainable ranching. The first two options, if appropriately applied, allow current stud breeders an opportunity to take a major leap forward and become part of the future. The third option is already becoming a reality and is driven by a grass-root need, but is dependent on stud breeders taking a major step forward and supplying the bulls required by this awakening market. The fourth option is currently reserved for those with an entrepreneurial spirit and creative flair. They are from the same mould as Lasater (Beefmaster), Harvey (Tuli), McLeod and Willoughby (Mashona) as well as many other unsung cattle heroes. The only difference is that they have a smaller world and greater use of technology (access to more genetic material) in their favour.

PUREBREEDING

There is a need for isolating and improving genotypes (breeds) with unique adaptive and productive attributes. But, this does not mean purebreeding for the sake of purebreeding. Are the Angus, Hereford and Sussex singularly so unique that they have to be bred separately with their own identifying trade marks (largely colour) that are unrelated to adaptation/productivity? Would it not be better to consider and breed them as a single genotype with regard to productivity in a temperate environment? At least they can then all be polled with good pigment. The same could be said for the Mashona, Nguni and Tuli.

Why not breed a superior Sanga by combining some, or all, of the sub-genotypes from which different ecotypes (depending on the different environments) can develop? Surely this allows greater opportunity for breeding a commercially attractive animal? Imagine a Sanga of solid colour (good pigment) that has an excellent meat: bone ratio (thanks to the Tuli) and is the hardiest (high relative intake, parasite/disease resistant) and most fertile (calving at 2+3 years) on veld. Another good example is the Conventional Composites. They all have a similar objective in a broadly similar environment. A much better animal can be bred by using the best genes from whatever source – Bonsmara, Beefmaster, Brangus, Simbra, Droughtmaster, Santa Gertrudis, Braford, etc.

BREEDING OF CROSSBRED BULLS

Here is a great opportunity for conventional stud breeders to expand their business and become part of a new dispensation. A Bonsmara breeder, for instance, could breed all his heifers to selected Nguni bulls/semen. The advantages are tremendous. Firstly, he would eliminate calving problems. Secondly, his young cows can be ranked (scored) according to fertility and cow efficiency allowing him the option of using the best for breeding pure Bonsmara. Thirdly, he has a commercially valuable product (veld productive) in the form of bulls (the market for such bulls is already there – it only requires further promotion) and heifers. The heifers provide a further opportunity for another breeder to add value by breeding them to another genotype bull (eg. Boran/Tuli bred by a Tuli breeder or Beefmaster/Boran bred by a Beefmaster breeder) and selling a four-breed combination bull (eg. Bonsmara/Nguni/Beefmaster/Boran or Bonsmara/Nguni/Boran/Tuli).

The only "problem" is that such thinking is too radical for the average purist stud breeder and officials at SA Stud Book who label such bulls as "bosbulle". My advice to those stud breeders who feel threatened by such thinking is that they must become the first to practise it. Here is a golden opportunity to transform a "problem" into an unfair advantage. Don't be part of a laager mentality.

CROSSBREEDING OF CROSSBREDS

This system of breeding will be the most appealing for ranchers. The only proviso is that purebred breeders and breeders of crossbred bulls (transformed stud breeders) do a good job of breeding bulls capable of siring progeny that will return maximum profit/ha. All that is required is for a rancher to obtain a bull genotype that will complement his crossbred cows and optimise hybrid vigour. A goal of **maximum sustainable profit/ha** should be the driving force behind bull breeding.

PUREBREEDING OF CROSSBREDS

What options are there for a breeder who has bred a genotype that is suitable for his conditions? Instead of continuing with crossbred bulls from an outside source he would be better off using homebred bulls selected on the basis of veld productivity. This way he will make more progress in further adapting a genotype to his specific conditions. Although his herd is "closed" he should not be bound by man-made rules preventing him using outside genes, if necessary, to achieve his goal of maximum sustainable profit/ha.

BULL SELECTION

A problem that will be encountered by ranchers looking for bulls is the absence of **meaningful** data. Raw ICP data have little, if any, connection with genetically determined fertility. Age at first calving only has significance when all heifers are bred at 14/15 months of age and only a few reconceive for the second calf at three years of age. Scrotal circumference has meaning only when considered in relation to body condition. Absolute measures of growth and size favour later maturing genotypes as does feed conversion efficiency (FCE) as conventionally measured. Making these inappropriate measurements more accurate from a genetic point of view (BLUP) only serves to baffle brains and accelerate change in the wrong direction. So what can a rancher, serious about veld productivity, do?

Having decided on the breed or genotype of bull in broad terms (Zebu, Sanga, Zebu/Sanga,etc.), select the breeder you think has the best chance of having the desired bulls. This may not be a recognised stud breeder. If a crossbred bull is sought then a commercial rancher would be the best option at present. Select before any bull calves are castrated since most breeders cull some of their best animals.   When a bull calf is running with its mother, calf/cow ratio and cow body condition (relative to other cows of similar efficiency) are easy to assess. The calf showing interest in other heifers/cows (particularly those on heat) will indicate his degree of sexual maturity. His physiological maturity (body condition/maturity rate/relative intake/grass conversion efficiency) can be gauged by the degree that the package is filled with meat – the "pony" (8-in-5 package) relative to the "draadkar" (9-in-10 package). If there are no obviously serious defects then the chances are very high that this "bosbul" is the best selection the buyer can make (in the absence of meaningful data) relative to a goal of **maximum sustainable profit/ha**.

HEIFER SELECTION

Assuming a breeder is making progress then the more heifers that can be retained in order to replace the less productive cows the greater the progress. A rancher starting off or in the process of increasing herd size can simultaneously improve his genotype by buying heifers (surplus to his requirements) and putting them through a selection process. Many good (the best?) weaner heifers end up in feedlots. If a rancher would buy these, breed them at around 14/15 months to the appropriate bull, retain those that are pregnant and sell the rest for breeding then he would have done effective selection for veld productivity. The greater the number of heifers tested and the lower the number that pass, the stricter the selection. Such a simple procedure is **many-fold more effective and scientific than the most proficient juggler of EPDs**.

13. PRACTICAL MANAGEMENT SUGGESTIONS

Ranching is the interface between man and cattle and as such should promote the dual role that cattle have to fulfill – efficient grass conversion and veld improvement. Any management practice outside the sphere of enhancing natural processes and accelerating natural selection is inappropriate. The following is an attempt to guide ranchers into simplifying management and creating harmony between cattle and their environment. The recommendations are based on personal experience in a tropical sourveld environment. However, many of the recommendations reflect principles that are valid in any environment.

INDIVIDUAL IDENTIFICATION

Some form of individual identification is essential. It should be simple and permanent. It is recommended to use ear notches cut shortly after birth, (Figure 13.1) that span from 1 to 1500. These can be prefixed (brand) by the year of birth/weaning (eg. 13 for 2013) and herd (A, B, C, etc.) where more than 1500 calves are born in a year. A permanent identification brand reflecting the ear notch can be branded at weaning. This can be a complete brand (eg. 13/566) or partial brand (eg. 13 denoting the year) with the individual identification number (566) read from the ear notch.

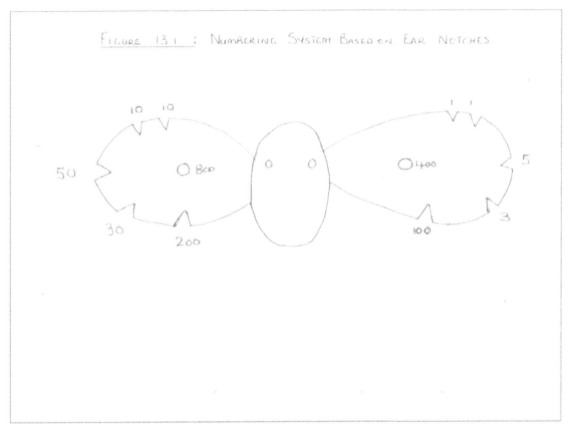

FIGURE 13.1: NUMBERING SYSTEM BASED ON EAR NOTCHES.

BRANDS

Identification (individual and herd) and performance brands can be branded on the animal. This can be in conjunction with written/electronic records. An example of performance records are those required by Veldmaster breeders (See Chapter 11: THE VELDMASTER (AFRICARNE)). Generally these brands can be applied to the hindquarter, forequarter, side, neck and cheek.

HERD COMPOSITION

In order to minimise grazing competition between individuals based on age, females should be classified into 3 groups – mature cows (4 years and older), young cows (2 and 3 years) and heifers (weaners and yearling). Wherever possible, high nutrient requirement groups (pregnant heifers) should be given preferential grazing.

COW: BULL RATIO

Generally speaking, the ratio is too narrow – too few cows per bull. Where multi-siring is practised and hormonally balanced, clinically and physically fit bulls are used the ratio of bull to cows can be doubled. The norm should be one mature bull per 50 cows instead of 25. This will not only cut bull costs, but will result in higher quality bulls being used.

BREEDING AGE

The goal should be to breed heifers as yearlings in order to calve at two years of age. Under current management and with many genotypes in use there are constraints to doing this. That is no excuse not to move in that direction. A starting point would be to at least allow individual heifers the chance to prove their ability to conceive at a young age by breeding all heifers at 14/15 months. Those that do calve at the age of two years and conceive again for their second calf at thee years should become part of a nucleus bull breeding herd. Those that do not are bred at a later stage in order to maintain herd size. An important proviso when breeding heifers is to ensure that the bulls in use do not contribute to calving problems. The appropriate genotype, calving season and herd management will allow successful yearling breeding.

BREEDING SEASON

The goal should be a 42 day breeding season. This can only occur when cows calve in good body condition (BCS of 3 on a scale 1 - 5). Cows should calve when body condition and nutrition are best. In seasonal rainfall environments this will be when grass is green. There will be slight variations, but generally speaking this will not be before the start of active grass growth in the majority of years. This is at least two to three months later than conventional calving.

In practice, in many situations, a longer (63 days) breeding season would be a good start. An additional breeding season may also be an initial requirement, particularly where the majority of heifers do not conceive at 14/15 months, but are capable of breeding at around 20 months as opposed to delaying breeding until the conventional 27 months. Although calving will occur at a time not conducive to lactating cows cycling the calves are weaned a month or two before the normal breeding season allowing a virtual 100% conception the second time around. Contrast this to a much lower reconception for cows calving a few months later as three-year-olds. An added advantage is that calves are weaned onto green grass and being older than their counterparts from three-year-old cows the result is much heavier weights.

DEHORNING

Dehorning of calves should be done at an early age (1 – 2 months). This, however, can be a very traumatic procedure, particularly when a hot iron is used. This is aggravated by screw-worm infestation in humid environments. A simple solution to dehorning is the breeding of naturally polled cattle.

WEANING

Calves have to be weaned and removed from their mothers some time before the next calf is born. The age at which this is done depends on circumstances. A producer not concerned about genetic selection and whose male calves have been castrated could decide to separate calves from their mothers at 9 – 10 months. A breeder intent on accurate selection will determine cow efficiency on the basis of the 6 month weight of calves (cows that reconceive early in the breeding season tend to wean calves early). The majority of calves can be weaned at 6 – 7 months and managed separately in order to ensure a meaningful 12 Maturity Score.

TICK CONTROL

The quicker ranchers get away from the wholesale use of poisonous dips the better. Rather than breeding dip resistant ticks we should be breeding tick resistant cattle. This is easier said than done for many ranchers in tick infested environments. The least that can be done in such situations is to reduce dipping and only use dip strategically. The first requirement is to stop dipping calves. All calves are born with a degree of pre immunity to tick borne diseases. If they are exposed to ticks transmitting a disease they do not generally develop the disease but acquire immunity which can be lasting if exposure is continuous. A major exception in Africa is sweating sickness which is caused by a toxin transmitted by ticks and generally only affecting young animals. Some African breeds, however, are genetically resistant to this disease. Another possibility is the use of vaccines to create immunity. These must be used with caution since there have been cases of calves dying from virulent, introduced strains of parasite which can also wreak havoc amongst adult "immune" cattle.

It is suggested that both breeding and management options be taken to reduce dipping whilst cautiously moving toward a goal of no dipping. Use bulls with the ability to repel ticks as well as inherent tick borne disease resistance. Do not dip calves. Animals with acquired immunity should only be treated strategically with the minimum of dip (spraying only affected areas). Those that did not acquire immunity as calves should be dipped as normal. Eventually a herd will be built up that requires no dipping or only strategic dipping.

It must be remembered that good body condition enhances the immune system which will reduce the incidence of all parasites and diseases including tick borne diseases. Previously immune animals can lose their immunity when under stress as indicated by poor body condition or that caused by movement to a new environment.

INTERNAL PARASITE CONTROL

From my experience I can say that animals in good body condition are capable of tolerating internal parasites. They only succumb to these parasites when they are in poor body condition. Therefore, in general, cattle adapted to their environment and managed for good body condition will not require dosing for internal parasites. Cattle that are under stress and in poor body condition can die from internal parasites if not treated.

The suggested strategy is to use bulls with inherently good body condition and inherent parasite resistance, manage for good body condition and treat and cull the occasional animal that is affected by parasites (indicated by poor body condition).

PARASITIC FLIES

Certain flies and other biting insects can transmit disease or negatively affect growth by being a nuisance. The tsetse fly in Africa transmits trypanosomiasis, which can be chronic or acute, and results in weight loss and ultimately death if not treated. Apart from the obvious solution of introducing cattle that are genetically resistant to the trypano-parasite (N'Dama from West Africa) veterinary authorities in Zimbabwe have developed a strategy that targets and kills the vector (tsetse fly). This is done by placing insecticide on treated nets (traps) at strategic places and attracting the fly to these traps by using acetone (mimicking cattle breath). This is an effective and environmentally "friendly" way of controlling a specific pest.

The horn fly is a blood-sucking pest found in tropical environments and some temperate areas with humid summers. Its greatest affect on cattle is from a nuisance point of view resulting in physical stress and reduced grazing time. A long term solution would be to breed for resistance. But, it appears that bulls with higher levels of testosterone attract more fly. Rather than selecting bulls with fewer flies on them select for lower stress (better body condition) as indicated by higher 12 Month Maturity Scores.

HANDLING

Cattle are a lot more intelligent than people give them credit for. Several examples come to mind. The first is where a herd of heifers was moved by foot from a paddock 80km to a railway station from where they travelled a further 200km. A year later, after the drought had broken, they retraced their journey. On approaching the paddock they had vacated a year earlier they stampeded to where the mineral lick had been placed. A particular cow (See Cover Photo) I had bonded with as a calf was moved over 500km away when I was forced off my land. Circumstances were such that we did not meet up again for a year. Upon hearing my voice from 100m away she came running out of the herd to meet me. A final example concerns a herd of 350 cows and calves that followed a herdsman for 5km to new grazing. The reason was that they were used to his call when opening up fresh grazing (UltraHigh Density Grazing) and responded to him calling them to move to the other side of the property.

When handling cattle we need to be aware of their intelligence and how they will react to circumstances. This applies in particular to the construction of handling facilities. In Africa, at least, where cattle are accustomed to regular handling I believe cattle kraals should be very simple. There is no need for curved, solid-sided crushes. Having experienced cattle filling a crush via a Bud Box convinces me even more that we tend to over elaborate. The Bud Box is named after Bud Williams, the American "cattle whisperer", who spent his life getting into the minds of cattle.

The Bud Box, approximately a 3½ x 6m rectangle, must be the basis of any form of cattle handling facility because it facilitates the movement of cattle into a crush or onto a loading ramp. The principle of how it works is very simple. When cattle enter a confined area through a gate their first reaction is to exit by the same gate. The handler following the small group of cattle (approximately 10 – 15) into the Bud Box closes the solid gate behind him and positions himself to the side allowing the cattle to loop around and escape into the crush (loading ramp) which is in line with the gate and at right angles to the Bud Box (See Photos 13.1 and 13.2)

The need for portable facilities becomes obvious when managing cattle in dense herds. A solution would be to have a permanent basic structure (Bud Box and small crush for A.I.) at convenient positions (water points). This would suffice for handling small numbers (A.I.; sick animals). When there is a need to handle a big herd portable panels can extend the existing facility.

PHOTO 13.1: *This photo was taken from inside a 3½ x 6m Bud Box with the photographer standing at the closed end of the rectangle. The cattle approach towards the photographer from the other side of the gate with the gate open. On closing the gate the handler stands to the right hand side of the Box allowing the cattle to loop around and into the race (crush) where my brother, Wessel, is standing.*

PHOTO 13.2: *This photo shows the Bud Box, with the gate open, to the left and cattle entering the race to the right. This herd had been worked a few days earlier and moved straight into the race (escape route) without even entering the Bud Box.*

IMMUNISATION

Immunisation and boosting the immune system is the field in which veterinarians should spend more time in contrast to treating symptoms. There are many good vaccines available for preventing many diseases and these should be used where necessary. However, we need vaccines that are safe and effective in preventing many tick borne diseases.

WATER

A constant, clean supply of water is essential. Surface water is good provided it is not muddy or polluted. When water is piped to troughs it is important to ensure that the flow and drinking area are sufficient for the demand and that the water is not fouled by animals climbing into troughs.

There is an inclination for ranchers managing cattle under ultrahigh stock density to opt for portable water troughs. They need to consider all the problems that could arise with such a system. I would opt for permanent and well constructed troughs, together with a basic handling facility, at convenient positions with cattle movement to and from the troughs limited to a road or corridor. One or two kilometres to water is not excessive for most situations.

SUPPLEMENTATION

Supplementation refers to the feeding of small amounts (less than 0.4% of live weight) of nutrients and rumen modifiers to increase grass intake or supply missing nutrients. Feeding much above this level may be profitable when finishing cattle off for slaughter, but results in feed substitution (less grass taken in) and is not effective as a rumen stimulant (increasing grass intake).

There are many areas where the energy content of the grass is high (consider the heat given off in a grass fire) and the protein value low (less than 4% crude protein) resulting in cattle becoming deficient in energy intake and losing body condition. This is the situation with low "octane" grazing in areas with a short wet season and long dry season. The only solution is to supplement with protein (natural and/or urea) and certain minerals in order to increase the rumen microbe population responsible for "digesting" fibrous grasses. The increase in grass intake of cattle can be in the order of 30% resulting in a positive energy balance.

The most obvious indication that cattle require a protein supplement is when the consistency of dung changes from sloppy to harder and drier. By watching the consistency of dung the amount and type of supplement can be modified.

There are various ways of feeding supplement ranging from a dry salt-regulated lick that is constantly available to the feeding of supplement in meal or cube form and throwing it out in a long line on the ground. I prefer the latter method as it removes the necessity of large amounts of salt and results in a more even intake on an individual basis. A more sophisticated system is the application of urea and minerals (such as phosphorus) via the water with a gadget that accurately regulates application depending on water flow (water intake). This is in common use in the northern parts of Australia.

A relatively recent development that came from Zimbabwe in the early 1990s is the administering of small amounts of polyethylene glycol (approximately 3g) on a daily basis in the water or supplement of cattle in order to neutralise the negative effects of tannin on the intake of browse. The result is much greater browse intake which has saved cattle from death in cases where there was no grass and only "unpalatable" browse from bushes and trees left. There is also a place for the administration of polyethylene glycol in the humid tropics of Latin America where forest/bush encroachment (natural succession) of planted pastures under conventional management is very rapid. This, in combination with UltraHigh Density Grazing, should dramatically increase stocking rate and maintain pastures in the predominantly grass stage.

ARTIFICIAL INSEMINATION

Any rancher serious about improving his cattle must make use of A.I. Even the largest and most extensive ranches have no excuse for not using A.I. – all they require is a nucleus herd of cows that are managed more intensively enabling A.I. The bulls produced from this herd are then used in the large, extensive herds.

The most difficult part of A.I. is getting cows to cycle and identifying them. A simple facility (Bud Box and crush) at the water point and teaser bulls or colour markers are all that is required. Heat synchronisation does have a place, but Fixed Time Insemination usually results in poor conception. With a 42 day breeding/calving season timed to coincide with optimum cow body condition at least 80 – 90% of lactating cows will be cycling before the start of the breeding season. This allows very effective synchronisation or the unsynchronised insemination of close to 100% of cows within the first 21 day heat cycle. Follow-up bulls can be used for the remaining 21 days at a very wide ratio of cows to bulls (1 bull per 100 -150 cows including those inseminated).

GRAZING MANAGEMENT

Grazing management is a vital part of ranch management. This is dealt with in PART III: VELD.

PART III: VELD

14. RANCHERS ARE CUSTODIANS OF THE VELD

The seasonal rainfall grasslands and savannahs of the world are degrading under modern management. This degradation is often insidious due to the resilience of nature and the time frame involved. Where it is recognised it is usually blamed on drought or too many animals. But, in many cases periods of drought and flood alternate within a season. This often occurs at pathetically low stocking rates. Another apparent enigma is that some of the worst cases of soil erosion due to water run-off can be seen in the drier areas.

The environment the voortrekkers and other pioneers encountered is very different to what we have today. There was an abundance and variety of plants and animals difficult to appreciate. Some of the large dongas in the Karoo that are now channelling silt-laden water to the sea were once perennial streams of clear water and habitat for hippo and fish (See: Manna in the Desert by Alfred de Jager Jackson). Transport operators using wagons had to put bells on their out spanned oxen in order to find them in the tall grass of the Karoo vleis.

Some documented cases show that current stocking rates are a fraction of what they were in the past. As an example, consider the case of a Bandelierkop property in the Limpopo Province of South Africa. Records indicate that in 1923 it carried 1200 head of cattle on 1000ha (Farmer's Weekly: 6 November 1992). It is doubtful whether the same area can carry 200 head under current conditions. One can carry on and on with examples from all over the world. Suffice to say that conventional management is contrary to natural systems and at loggerheads with nature.

There is a degree of ignorance and an even greater degree of arrogance in man's view of nature. The general view is that man must replace natural systems with those of his own making in order to gain time and appropriate as much money as possible. The rancher is unique amongst agriculturists by measuring productivity relative to an animal unit as opposed to a land unit. Apart from being poor economics it leads directly to veld degradation – a common way of increasing production per animal is to allow them to selectively overgraze.

PHOTOS 14.1 and **14.2**: *One of the consequences of inappropriate grazing management – extremely ineffective rainfall. Exposed soil in seasonal rainfall environments leads to excessive run-off and high evaporation (right) resulting in once perennial rivers (left) becoming gullies that channel silt-laden water to the sea. Droughts and floods alternate within a season.*

PHOTOS 14.3 and **14.4** *depict stagnant ecosystem processes. On the left are a few desert grasses growing in a 600mm rainfall area. The reason for this is an ineffective rainfall due to capped and compacted soil. On the right is a mass of dead grass (pulled out by hand) resulting from limited grazing and low Animal Impact. In both cases soil fertility is in decline with very little photosynthesis (solar energy capture) taking place.*

Such a philosophy of control and interference in nature has led to the current problems encountered by ranchers. Foremost amongst them are low stocking rates, poor reproduction (poor inherent body condition) and excessive inputs in the form of feed and chemicals resulting in extremely low interest on capital investment, particularly in South Africa. Much of the "productivity" achieved by past and current generations is the result of appropriating biological capital that has been built up by natural systems over centuries. The result is a continually declining capital base (biological capital) with less interest (profit).

We do not own land. Those who are privileged to manage land are its custodians. We have a moral obligation to improving it. Unfortunately this obligation is generally taken too lightly.

In the context of veld the major penalty for mismanagement is a low stocking rate. All that is required to redeem this is an about-turn in management (simulate the grass - grazer - predator relationship) plus many more mouths and hoofs (a limiting factor in most situations is animal numbers). Academics and most land managers will consider such an assertion to be absurd.

That is because they have never implemented time-controlled high Animal Impact and Non-Selective Grazing. In general, it appears that the redeemable stocking rate is two to four times the conventionally accepted rate – a truly amazing reward for good stewardship.

15. RANCHERS HAVE BEEN MISLED

ACADEMICS HAVE GENERALLY MADE WRONG CONCLUSIONS

Nothing much in terms of veld management research and recommendations has changed since the 1950s. All official management systems revolve around selective grazing/overgrazing followed by long term rest to counter the negative effects of animals under inappropriate management. Additional management tools are fire (particularly on sourveld) and chemicals for weed and bush control. An exception is work done on the introduction of nitrogen fixing legumes to planted pastures and veld. In Africa, Dr. John Clatworthy from the Grasslands Research Station in Marondera, Zimbabwe has been at the forefront of this work using tropical legumes originating from Latin America. There is still much scope for further development, particularly in South Africa, with little progress at the official level other than with lucerne.

Although Allan Savory (not a conventional researcher) has recently contributed greatly to our understanding of brittle (seasonal rainfall) environments, the concept was understood many years ago. The late Prof. Scott from the University of Natal was aware of the problems presented by such environments from work he was doing on veld management in the 1950s (The Grasses and Pastures of South Africa: Central News Agency 1955). He said: *"Under our conditions of dry winters, the dead parts of tufts do not tend to form humus but form a thatch. By the end of the third season most of the ungrazed tufts are dead and can be pulled out quite easily. Weeds begin to grow in these dead tufts and so the veld deteriorates. It is necessary to remove any accumulation of ungrazed tufts to prevent such deterioration. Although a case could be made for burning under such conditions,* **it must always be remembered that burning is simply a method of disposing of herbage which could have been used at some time under a more efficient system of management**".

It is unfortunate, and an indictment against universities and other institutions, that more than 50 years later they have still not come up with "a more efficient system of management". The fact that pioneering ranchers are using high Animal Impact and Non-Selective Grazing to improve their veld and its productivity appears to be ignored or ridiculed. Their best response is that "this approach is not currently advocated by the Department of Agriculture because there is no long term data to support these contentions" (Farmer's Weekly: 19 July 2002; p.26). Have these institutions abrogated their responsibilities? When are they going to make an effort to acquire their own data and look into these "contentions"? The research necessary to prove or disprove the claims regarding high Animal Impact and severe grazing is extremely simple and cheap. An open mind and a little bit of humility are the main requirements.

If it were not for individuals like John Acocks and Allan Savory together with many pioneering ranchers in southern Africa we would still be looking for "a more efficient system of management". It is a fact that universities, colleges and research stations have been responsible for very useful information. It is also a fact that no professor or researcher has been able to put all available information (official or otherwise) together in order to create a functioning whole. This is less the fault of individuals and more the fault of our education system. **Research stations must become model ranches** and professors must first become model ranchers. If this is not achieved we will continue to be misled by academics who **learn more and more about less and less until they know everything about nothing.**

TALL GRASS AND SCATTERED TREES MEANS GOOD VELD

It is not only ranchers that have been fooled by the presence of tall grass and scattered trees as an indication of good veld. I was in the company of a group of ranchers and self-styled "range scientists" from the University of Natal viewing veld situated between a main road and railway line at Nsiza, Zimbabwe that was not grazed but occasionally burnt owing to its location. The veld had a pleasing appearance to the eye and compared to the adjacent mismanaged ranch looked healthy. This site was chosen as an example of what the "range scientists" believed to be ideal veld. Having seen firsthand what veld under time-controlled high Animal Impact and Non-Selective Grazing looks like, I pulled out a tuft of moribund grass (there had been no fire for a few years) and pointed to the fact that there were no seedlings or young plants (except where a grader making a firebreak had disturbed soil). Several ranchers nodded in agreement. The more vocal of the visitors who had come to Zimbabwe to teach us how veld should be managed retorted: "As a range scientist I am telling you this is good veld". Needless to say, neither this individual nor anyone else in his group responded to an invitation to visit my property where stocking rate had been trebled after two years of UltraHigh Density Grazing.

I relate the above for two reasons. The first is that we all need to be humble and keep our feet on the ground. The second is that we need to judge the health of veld by looking at much more than grass and trees. Understanding that we are managing a whole consisting of grass, grazers and the predatory effect would be a step in the right direction. The above incident highlights the discrepancy between scientist knowledge and, in this case, rancher knowledge. Scientists must find a way of getting more cow dung on their feet.

TOO MANY ANIMALS RESULT IN DETERIORATION

The most important precept of conventional veld management is a conservative stocking rate. It is believed that exceeding an officially recommended stocking rate for a particular area will result in veld degradation. At, or below, the recommended stocking rate veld will apparently remain stable, particularly with regular long rest periods (usually not less than a year) in addition to the possible use of fire. Such an approach will satisfy ranchers who measure success in terms of production/animal. On the surface it may appear that the veld is not deteriorating judging by the amount of material that will have to be burnt on sourveld in addition to the recovery of veld after a season's rest. What is certain is that production/ha and return on capital investment will be low. What is also certain, but only apparent to those with experience in time-controlled high Animal Impact (veld degradation can be insidious), is that the ecosystem is functioning very poorly and that conventional stocking rates are a fraction of the potential.

As will be seen, stocking rate/carrying capacity is a dependent variable (influenced by management) and not an independent variable (influencing veld production) as suggested by conventional wisdom and as such does not influence veld degradation *per se*. **Many more animals are required to improve the veld**, but they need to be managed appropriately.

GRAZE LIGHTLY

Ranchers are often advised to graze veld lightly (utilise plants lightly and to the same degree), particularly after a drought. How is this possible on veld with a variety of different grasses and even grasses from the same species with varying palatability? This may be possible some day when cows have been taught or bred to utilise all plants to the same degree or only graze the older plants as suggested by a researcher. Until then, however, cows at low stock density on most veld types will choose to graze certain grasses severely and leave others untouched.

In an effort not to deplete grass root energy reserves completely after grazing and allow grasses to recover quicker it is recommended to graze all grass plants down to 50% - "take half and leave half". As just discussed, this is not possible (except, **possibly**, on some monoculture pastures and unique veld types). On tropical sourveld, at least, the result is a stocking rate 50% lower than carrying capacity. The 50% utilisation is in total plant material (0% to 100% variation in utilisation of individual plants, often of the same species) and not in 50% utilisation of individual grasses. Where veld is afforded a recovery period, the previously grazed grasses will be grazed again and the more mature grasses will remain ungrazed. The only solution in such a situation is doubling stocking rate and implementing time - controlled high Animal Impact and severe grazing of all grasses.

TREATING SYMPTOMS

Owing to the lack of control over each hoof and each mouth, as well as the fact that most researchers and advisors are out of touch with reality, management is reactive. This amounts to treating the symptoms and not the causes. Treating symptoms becomes addictive and expensive because the symptoms recur.

MORIBUND GRASS

Dead and moribund grass is the result of too few animals and a low stock density. Burning does invigorate moribund grass and increases palatability. This can be a wise decision before implementing UltraHigh Density Grazing, particularly on sourveld. But, burning leads to bare ground resulting in soil surface capping and increased water run-off. There is also a decrease in grass yield. Both these effects are exaggerated in a dry environment.

The need for burning is usually the result of too few animals and low stock density. Where this is corrected there will be no moribund or dead grass, but many seedlings and young, vigorous plants.

PHOTOS 15.1 *and* **15.2**: *Sparsely spaced and moribund grass plants of a palatable species (Cenchrus cilliaris) in the Chaco region of Paraguay. The photos were taken towards the end of their short (4 month) dry season in a "drought" year. Low stocking rates (more than 50% of plants unutilised) and low stock densities are the cause of the situation. In Photo 15.2 there is sparsely spaced moribund grass to the left of the fence and vigorous green grass, of the same species, to the right of the fence. The difference in vigour and colour of the grass on the right is due to regular mowing of the grass in the road servitude. Grass needs to be defoliated to remain vigorous.*

ENCROACHING BUSH

In many areas of the world trees are an essential component of veld. The same applies to many forbs, particularly legumes. In the wet seasonal rainfall tropics forest or woodland is the climax vegetation that requires unique management practices to maintain a sub-climax of grass. But, why do trees, bushes and weeds encroach on savannah and grassland?

The main reason for bush encroachment is a lack of grass vigour. This is due to **low Animal Impact, overgrazing** and **overresting** of grass. A secondary reason is insufficient browsing. The surest way to ensure bush or weed encroachment in seasonal rainfall grassland and savannah is the total resting of land - removing all severe grazers and preventing fire.

PHOTOS 15.3 and **15.4**: *The surest way to weaken or kill grass in seasonal rainfall environments is not to defoliate it. Depending on environment, grass is replaced entirely by bush (left) or partially by weeds (right). In the plot on the left cattle had been removed for 14 years and on the right for 9 years.*

In conventional veld management the land is partially rested (low stocking rate, low Animal Impact and selective grazing). The result is poor grass vigour allowing tap rooted plants such as trees and bushes to establish. In addition to this, little browsing occurs with even less physical damage to trees. Contrast this to what happens under UltraHigh Density Grazing.

It **may** be necessary, in extreme cases, to initially address bush encroachment by treating the symptom (targeted chemical or mechanical eradication). Without treating the cause, however, bush encroachment will recur. The cause is treated by applying time-controlled high Animal Impact and Non-Selective Grazing. In certain circumstances, such as with thorn bush encroachment, the use of goats in addition to cattle may be necessary to utilise and control bush. In many cases cattle under UltraHigh Density Grazing will control bush. In wet and humid seasonal rainfall environments (for example, Central Africa) a combination of high Animal Impact in addition to the occasional use of a hot fire may be necessary to maintain savannah. Fire, in the drier areas, is too damaging for it to be used other than as a one-off occurrence (hot fire to damage encroaching bush). There is little, or no, need for it in the presence of high Animal Impact.

REDUCE ANIMAL NUMBERS

A foundational belief of conventional wisdom is that animal numbers *per se* determine whether veld deteriorates or not. It is believed that each environment can carry a certain number of animals per unit of land with degradation only occurring above this magical number. The result is that when veld is visibly deteriorating or individual animal performance is not up to expectation the advice is to decrease cattle numbers. Rather than being a one-off adjustment (if stocking rate was an independent variable) it becomes a continual process as evidenced by a Zimbabwe Cattleman of the Year who acknowledged that his stocking rate had declined by 50% over a period of 25 years.

Researchers and ranchers need to understand that carrying capacity/stocking rate is a **dependent variable** – it is dependent on many factors that can be influenced by the management of hoofs and mouths. Some of these factors include effective rainfall, soil aeration, nutrient cycle, plant succession, plant density, veld utilisation and effective photosynthesis. That is why stocking rates can be increased manyfold by appropriate management.

BARE AREAS

Bare areas that form in certain seasonal rainfall environments as well as a decrease in plant density are conventionally blamed on too many animals. The first recommendation would be to decrease animal numbers drastically or to remove animals completely. This is reacting to a symptom without addressing the cause. The cause of a decrease in plants is inappropriate management (too low Animal Impact over an extended period) and not too many animals. A concentration of hard hoofs at appropriate intervals is what is required to cultivate the soil in order to create conditions conducive to the establishment of grasses and forbs.

NEUTRALISING THE NEGATIVE EFFECTS OF SELECTIVE OVERGRAZING

There seems to be an unwritten law in academic circles that domestic livestock are inherently bad for the veld and that management must be aimed at minimising or negating these effects. This is attempted through maintaining low stocking rates and even reducing animal numbers, burning excess grass, long (year-long) recovery periods after an extended period of overgrazing, mechanically establishing grass and mechanical/chemical bush control. In many instances cattle are replaced by "natural" grazers such as buffalo and wildebeest in fenced areas without the presence of predators. None of these practices are sustainable in the medium to long term.

NONE AS BLIND AS THOSE WHO DON'T WANT TO SEE

The Establishment seem to believe that that they have a monopoly when it comes to the truth. Any idea originating outside their sphere of influence is ridiculed, dismissed or ignored. This is particularly true of universities and agricultural institutes. Let me explain:

- Since the 1960s John Acocks together with the Howells (Hillside, Springfontein) and others from South Africa have tried to implement high Animal Impact and severe grazing in the form of Non-Selective Grazing (NSG) mainly with sheep in arid country. Using their own livestock and own money they experimented on farm scale and, at least, indicated to the sceptics that there was a way of reversing veld degradation whilst carrying many more animals resulting in an increase in profitability. Here was an opportunity for serious minded researchers to test the claims made in regard to Animal Impact and severe grazing and, if valid, come up with a practical solution to increase stock density to the required level under extensive conditions. The half-hearted research that was done yielded nothing other than the feeble comment that "this approach is not currently advocated by the Department of Agriculture because there is no long term data to support these contentions" (Farmer's Weekly, 19 July 2002, p. 26). Nothing has changed after 50 years.

- During the 1970s a trial was carried out on Charter Estate, Zimbabwe. This involved a Control (1 herd/4 paddocks) that was compared with a Short Duration Grazing system (double stocking rate; 1 herd/16 paddocks) under the control of Allan Savory. After 7 years it was conclusively proved by the researchers that stocking rate could be doubled without veld degradation. It was also shown that profitability increased by 28% even with a decline in animal production (13% lower calving rate; 10% lower weaning weight). Incredibly, the general consensus (amongst ranchers and academics) was that the "Savory System" was a failure, largely due to the drop in individual animal production. I have often wondered what the outcome would have been if this was a trial done on cropland with double plant population resulting in 28% greater profitability.

Those involved in this trial missed an opportunity to question conventional wisdom and carry out further research to find a way to minimise, or eliminate, the drop in animal performance that was entirely due to poorer nutrition (Non-Selective Grazing). The factors that should have been considered include the number of paddocks/herd (stock density), increased supplementation, cow genotype and production in sync with seasonal variation in nutrition.

- In February of 1993 I paid a private visit to a man by the name of Rudi Radley living near Senekal, South Africa. This was in response to an article on how he was able to drastically increase his stocking rate by the use of portable electric fences in order to increase stock density and control time. Here was a man who demonstrated how cattle could be controlled in order to create constant herd effect on a ranch scale. Although an Extension Agent was involved, who clearly saw the positive results, no-one further up the hierarchy seemed to pay any notice – they were probably still waiting for "long term data to support these contentions" of high Animal Impact and Non-Selective Grazing.

-      On January 12, 1995 I implemented UltraHigh Density Grazing on my property near Karoi, Zimbabwe. Within a matter of weeks stocking rate was doubled, in the driest year on record, owing to improved veld utilisation. Two years later stocking rate was treble the norm. In 2002 it was possible to carry four times the norm.

-      In 1997 the *Cattle Producers Association of Zimbabwe* sponsored a team of self-styled "range scientists" led by professors from the University of Natal in South Africa to visit the country and inform cattlemen of new developments in the field of veld management (Basically amounting to one year of abuse followed by one year of total animal withdrawal). Despite being aware of what I was doing and very critical of any form of high Animal Impact and severe grazing not one of them responded to my invitation to visit my property where treble animal numbers were already being carried. I suppose in their case it would be true to say that "what you don't see doesn't hurt". Do these gentlemen realise what a disservice they have done cattlemen worldwide?

PHOTO 15.5: *Despite the dire predictions of many this is what the veld looked like on my property after 7 years of high Animal Impact and Non-Selective Grazing (Karoi, Zimbabwe). At this stage stocking rate had been trebled.*

- Several years ago the management of Beefcor near Bronkhorstspruit, South Africa (manage 40,000 weaner calves under UltraHigh Density Grazing) invited, and sponsored, the University of Pretoria to monitor veld changes under high Animal Impact and severe grazing. In addition, the university set up burnt and mown strips to be compared with intensively grazed strips. After a few years of monitoring, with absolutely conclusive results in favour of animal impact (See Photo: 15.6) the exercise was terminated. Nothing further was heard from the academics involved. Another squandered opportunity by those who can't see or don't want to see.

PHOTO 15.6: *Beefcor/University of Pretoria experimental plot showing recovery after burning (foreground) and extremely high Animal Impact (background). The results favouring high Animal Impact over burning and mowing were visually so obvious that anyone with an open mind could see. Yet, for some reason, the results in the hands of the academics concerned were never made public or followed up on.*

16.   100 MILLION SPRINGBOK IN ONE HERD

There are many historical reports of pristine grasslands and savannahs teeming with large herds of grazers. Areas that come to mind are the Prairies of America, the grasslands of South Africa, the savannas of East Africa and the Steppes of Asia. The most amazing account refers to herds of up to 100 million Springbok (estimated from the width and length of the herd) moving through the arid grasslands of the Karoo of South Africa (now predominantly shrubs) leaving "devastation" in their path . Any thinking person must pose the question: Was this impact responsible for the productive grasslands modern man inherited and is it still necessary today?

PHOTO 16.1: *A cattle round-up on King Ranch. Texas. In lieu of migrating wildlife ranchers will need to use cattle to create occasional or, depending on environment, continuous herd effect. This can be done by herding with herdsmen or with some form of electric fencing.*

YOU CAN'T SWEETEN A CUP OF TEA WITH A FEW GRAINS OF SUGAR

Environments require a threshold to be exceeded in terms of impact (physical disturbance of soil surface and plants) before any positive change can occur to benefit the ecosystem and, in particular, grass growth and grass density. This is akin to trying to sweeten a cup of tea (coffee for Americans). Adding a few grains of sugar, as attempted by some researchers, does not help. Depending on conditions, anything from a teaspoon to several teaspoons will be required. This can be seen in the accompanying photograph (Photo: 16.2) where a clear boundary is visible between low impact (predominantly shrubs) and very high impact (predominantly grass). The challenge is to exceed this threshold – below and up to this threshold nothing much changes; above this threshold a new world is created.

HIGH IMPACT REQUIRED EVERY FEW YEARS IN AN ARID ENVIRONMENT

Unlike seasonally humid environments with high fibre grasses where continually high Animal Impact is essential, arid environments with compacted soils require infrequent, heavy impact. I have personally experienced areas that changed from shrub to grass in one treatment of high impact and that remained in a grassland state for several years without any further impact. This suggests that although it is much more difficult to create herd effect (extremely high stock density) in arid environments it may only be an occasional (every few years?) requirement. The intervening period can be managed at stock densities required for Non-Selective Grazing.

PHOTO 16.2: *The effect of a single treatment of extremely high Animal Impact on the property of Dirkie Ackerman, Venterstad, South Africa. This occurred when a large flock of sheep was contained by an electric fence for a few hours whilst groups of sheep were being worked in the handling facility. The border between low (shrubs) and high impact (grass) is clearly visible and remained so for several years. This indicates that, although very high impact is essential in this arid environment, it only needs to be an occasional occurrence.*

17. "SOUTH AFRICA IS OVERGRAZED AND UNDERSTOCKED" - JOHN ACOCKS

In the early 1950s John Acocks stated that *"South Africa is overgrazed and understocked"*. This must be one of the most profound statements ever made in the field of natural resource management. Then, as now, very few people understand the meaning. The answer to the riddle of degradation and rehabilitation of hundreds of millions of hectares of seasonal rainfall grasslands all over the world lies in understanding what was meant by this simple statement.

Working as a botanist, charting the different Veld Types of South Africa, Acocks was in a unique position to see, at ground level, what was happening to the veld. Amongst the things he observed was that at the conventionally recommended low stocking rate and long occupation period in a paddock certain plants were grazed continuously whilst others were largely untouched. The result was a change in grass and shrub species composition in favour of the less palatable, and largely less productive, species.

The crux of this statement is that with conventional (low stock density) management a percentage of plants are overgrazed (continuously re-grazed without sufficient recovery). Simultaneously, a percentage of plants are left unutilised due to insufficient animals (Remember, a precept of conventional management is low stock numbers in order to "protect" the veld and improve animal nutrition). The solution to the problem of selective overgrazing, as suggested by Acocks, is increased animal numbers, higher stock density (more paddocks per herd) and sufficient time for plants to recover after being grazed. The challenge was finding stockmen willing to implement Non-Selective Grazing as well as the creation of sufficient paddocks. The first challenge was overcome immediately; the second challenge would only be fully overcome 40 years later.

NON-SELECTIVE GRAZING (NSG)

Several South African stockmen, under the influence or guidance of John Acocks, started implementing Non-Selective Grazing on their properties in the 1950s and 1960s in an attempt to reverse desertification and improve the species composition of their veld. The majority were situated in the semi-arid to arid south-central and southern parts of the sub-continent. All showed a love for the land and a passion to restore the veld to its former glory – even at great personal expense. This was in contrast to the indifference or opposition from official circles. Many names come to mind (Nel, Trollip, Mathews, Mc Naughton, Mc Cabe, Hobson, Lund, Hobbs, Minnaar, Kroon), but the most prominent amongst them are the husband and wife team of Len and Denise Howell of Springfontein in the semi-arid (450mm annual rainfall) southern Free State Province of South Africa.

What really made the Howells stand out was the detailed records of farm-scale experimentation and the publicity this received (Denise Howell was a trained journalist). Using sheep and up to 12 paddocks per flock they were able to double stocking rate and dramatically improve their veld. Eventually they also acquired cattle in order to better utilise the large amount of grass, relative to shrubs, they were able to grow.

The general conclusions that were drawn from the pioneering work with NSG are:

- Forcing animals to graze non-selectively increased stocking rate tremendously (doubling was common) and improved species composition.

- Animals grazed non-selectively experienced a decline in their nutritional status relative to those grazing selectively. This was reflected in a decrease in individual performance (reproduction, daily gain, wool yield).

- The consensus among proponents of NSG was that increasing the number of paddocks per herd would enable better time control resulting in improved individual animal performance as well as greater veld improvement.

In retrospect, the work of Acocks and the early NSG pioneers provided the important breakthrough required for there to be harmony between grazers, under the control of man, and veld. However, the baton would need to go through the hands of a few more people with there feet firmly on the ground. Not a single academic would be included in this relay. Some seemed determined to spoil the race.

SHORT DURATION GRAZING (SDG)

Allan Savory, an ecologist working in the central African region encompassing present day Zimbabwe and Zambia, was the first to highlight the importance of the grass-grazer-predator whole in terms of grassland health. Initially he was of the opinion that the only solution to veld degradation on ranches was to replace livestock with game. However, the ideas of Acocks eventually convinced him that the only practical solution was to mimic a grass-grazer-predator whole using cattle in lieu of buffalo and wildebeest. This led to his involvement with cattle ranchers from the mid-1960s in, what was then referred to as, Short Duration Grazing (SDG).

Where the emphasis in NSG was in non-selectivity of grazing the emphasis in SDG, initially at least, was in relatively short periods of grazing (a few days) with relatively long periods of recovery (a few weeks). These periods of occupation and absence also varied between the growing (shorter) and non-growing (longer) seasons. Savory always stressed the need for more paddocks per herd in order to increase Animal Impact and stock density as well as to improve time control. The problem was the physical and economic limitation to creating many conventional paddocks. Generally, paddock numbers varied between 4 and 8 with the most advanced layout having 42 paddocks per herd.

Although some form of time control limited overgrazing with beneficial effects on grass vigour and increased stocking rates, the critics cited poor individual animal performance as a drawback to SDG. This became the logjam to progress and seemingly the sole criterion whereby grazing systems were evaluated. It was to become the albatross around Savory's neck which he thought could be overcome with paddock configuration (Wagon wheel layout; Cell layout) and a different decision making process (Holistic Resource Management; Holistic Management) which he formulated after moving to the USA.

THE CHARTER TRIALS

Owing to the great deal of interest created by SDG amongst ranchers in Zimbabwe, the management of Charter Estate, south-east of Harare, set aside land and cattle for a grazing trial. The objective was to see whether more cattle than conventionally recommended could be carried without veld degradation and whether there was any economic benefit in doing so.

As a control, Charter Estate managed a herd of cattle under a 1 Herd: 4 Paddock grazing system amounting to continuous grazing with seasonal rests and a burn every four years. This was compared to a *"Poor Man Savory"* (1 herd - 8 Paddocks) and a *"Rich Man Savory"* (1 herd - 16 paddocks), both stocked at double the conventional rate and under the guidance of Allan Savory. Biological monitoring was done by Dr. John Clatworthy and financial monitoring by Dr. Stan Parsons.

After 7 years the trial was terminated with the following conclusions and viewpoints:

- Cattle can be managed at double the conventional stocking rate, on this specific veld type, without veld degradation.

- The limited time control and insufficient stock density with 8 to 16 paddocks per herd did not result in veld improvement relative to the Control.

- At double stocking rate where cattle are forced to graze less selectively there is a drop in individual performance. In this case calving rate dropped from 80% to 67% and weaning weight by 10%.

- Gross Margin per hectare increased by 28% where stocking rate was doubled.

- Return on capital at double stocking rate and poorer individual animal performance was similar to the Control.

NO VELD DEGRADATION WITH "TOO MANY ANIMALS"

The fact that there was no veld deterioration at double the conventionally recommended stocking rate should have shaken the foundations of accepted grazing management recommendations since conservative stocking is the basic tenet of conventional veld management thinking. That this did not happen highlights the enigma of the human mind. Our minds can be either creative or obstructive, as in this case.

STOCKING RATE IS MORE IMPORTANT THAN ANIMAL PERFORMANCE

The fact that the number of animals on a piece of land had a greater influence on profitability than each individual's performance should have shaken the foundations of cattle breeding, since conventionally, everything revolves around breeding high performing cattle. If animal scientists had taken stock of this fact then we would not be in the situation where cattle are bred to be lean and "efficient" and fed in order to be "productive".

CROSSROAD

Contrary to what everyone said at the time, I believe the Charter Trials were highly successful. Veld management had reached a crossroad. There was absolutely no doubt that veld degradation was not determined by the number of animals, *per se*, on a piece of land. There was also no doubt about the fact that more animals made more money. The questions that should have been asked, and answered, were:

- What degree of stock density would be required to **improve** the veld and **maximise** stocking rate? If high Animal Impact and severe grazing are found to be beneficial, how would it be possible to create hundreds to thousands of "paddocks" per herd in practice?

- If nutrition was the limiting factor in terms of animal performance, how can body condition be improved? What would be the effect of high stock density (frequent moves per day onto fresh grazing), genotype (inherently good body condition), improved supplementation and production in sync with seasonal variation in nutrition?

It is extremely unfortunate that no-one in research made any attempt to answer the questions staring them in the face. It is also unfortunate that Savory sought intangible answers and alienated many independent thinkers who could have helped him find tangible answers. I am absolutely convinced that we can now move on from where the Charter Trial was left in limbo, so to speak.

SAVORY AND HOLISTIC MANAGEMENT

I believe the greatest contribution Allan Savory has made is the new direction he gave ranchers in regard to veld management. This will be his legacy and not a "new decision making framework" (Holistic Resource Management; Holistic Management). Although it is true that "nothing will change until your thinking changes", it is also true that something tangible is needed to change your thinking.

THE GRASS-GRAZER-PREDATOR RELATIONSHIP

The grass-grazer-predator relationship that Savory has bought to our attention is tangible and is the answer to veld management. What was lacking was total animal control in terms of stock density and time. This is where the focus should have been – not on goal setting and formal decision making.

THE ABSTRACT – GOAL SETTING AND DECISION MAKING

I strongly believe that because Allan failed to fully appreciate the real logjam – lack of animal control – he went off at a tangent and sought redress in the intangible – goal setting and decision making. At the outset, I must make it absolutely clear that I fully endorse the importance of a clear goal, because without it there are many roads that lead to nowhere. I also endorse the absolute importance of appropriate decision making. But, formal goal setting and decision making as attempted in Holistic Resource Management/Holistic Management is generally counter productive. What is intended to be a decision making process becomes an indecision making process. I have experienced many examples of this.

I also accept the importance of a wider goal encompassing the social issues of a business and that they should be addressed. However, when working within the context of the grass-grazer-predator whole an appropriate goal, in terms of managing the ecosystem, is **maximum sustainable profit/ha**. Surely no rancher has a problem with this. This places the focus on the physical aspects of management. There will be no need to "re-visit goals" and "check your weak link". These aren't the sort of activities ranchers with cow dung on their boots want, or need, to do.

I will always credit Allan for his insight into the interaction between the hoofs and mouths of severe grazers together with the herding effect of predators and a healthy grassland/savannah ecosystem. We owe him a great deal of gratitude for his persistence in trying to make scientists and ranchers understand that we need to manage livestock differently in order to improve the veld. I will also give him credit for having planted these seeds in my mind at a very early and impressionable age. These seeds, together with those planted by other independent thinkers like Jan Bonsma (opposed to Savory's ideas) and Tom Lasater eventually led to the harmonising of apparently irreconcilable philosophies.

FEET BACK ON THE GROUND

From the late 1970s to the mid-1990s Holistic Movement *a la* Savory went into limbo as far as real progress on the ground was concerned. The 12th of January 1995 was the turning point. From this date onwards the ranching world was made aware of the practical, and economic, feasibility of maintaining high stock density and creating constant, or strategic, herd effect. This was the breakthrough required to enable ranchers to implement **appropriate decisions** and achieve their goals. I must emphasise that, without this breakthrough, we would still be sitting around tables going through the motions of formal goal setting and decision making. **Let us rather grow more grass and breed and manage cattle for more efficient grass conversion.**

18. MAKING TWO BLADES OF GRASS GROW WHERE ONLY ONE GREW BEFORE

The only way we can grow more grass, in a sustainable way, is to mimic nature. Allan Savory made us aware of how a natural grassland/savannah ecosystem functions and how we can mimic such a system using livestock in lieu of game.

GRASS-GRAZER-PREDATOR

All the major grasslands and savannahs of the seasonal rainfall areas of the world developed under large herds of grazers in the presence of pack hunting predators. The result was a symbiotic relationship between grass, grazer and predator. Large herds of grazers bunched up in fear of predators grazed, trampled, dunged, urinated and moved constantly. In their wake soil and plants regenerated resulting in an efficiently functioning ecosystem. This is akin to an orchestra (grass and grazers) with a conductor (predators). Remove the conductor, as the case is in modern management, and there is complete discord. In order to return to harmony, modern management needs to re-introduce the predatory effect and control time and timing.

ONE PLUS ONE IS NOT TWO

In the mechanical world one plus one is equal to two. In the natural world there are too many interacting forces for the result of different actions to be a simple addition. The following examples illustrate this.

SALIVA

Work done in the USA (Reardon,P.O and Merril,L.B : Proc. Int. Rangeland Cong. 1; 396 – 397) proves that thiamine (Vitamin B1) in the saliva of cattle stimulates the re-growth of grazed grasses. The effect is greater on low fertility soil and under conditions of excessive defoliation. In trials on sandy soils of poor fertility, grasses that were cut and treated with saliva resulted in 79% faster re-growth than control plots that were cut but not treated with saliva.

This example is only a small part of the picture and clearly indicates the symbiotic relationship between grass and grazers. What about all the other effects of the animal (dunging, urinating, trampling, etc.) on the ecosystem if done in an orchestrated fashion (concentration, time and timing)?

PHOTOS 18.1 and 18.2: The symbiotic relationship between cattle and grass is evident in these photos. Pale green and thin leafed grass (left) is indicative of poor soil aeration and a poor nutrient cycle between soil and plants. This was rectified in Photo 18.1 by high Animal Impact. The results, two years later, can be seen in Photo 18.2.

BROWSING

Cattle normally do browse some bushes and trees at certain times. Under conventional management the intensity of browsing is low owing to the inhibiting effect of tannin in the leaf. Experiments done by the Wildlife Department of the University of Pretoria showed clearly that high tannin concentration in the leaves of trees is a defense mechanism against over browsing and that it is related to time. Upon browsing, the tannin content increases until a stage is reached where the browse becomes extremely unpalatable and even poisonous to animals. After a certain period of time without browsing tannin levels return to normal. However, when cattle are grazing at very high densities and moved frequently onto fresh grazing with a long intervening period of time they browse voraciously – even to the extent of physically damaging trees (See accompanying photos). My assumption is that browse under such conditions exhibits low tannin levels for the period that animals occupy an area. No-one could have predicted such an outcome. It only becomes apparent upon physically doing it.

This relationship between tannin content and time can now be used to increase browse utilisation (effectively increase stocking rate) and control bush encroachment. It can lead to a breakthrough in managing pasture established after clearing tropical forest as is done in Central and South America. The problem here, for ranchers, is the fast regeneration of forest. UltraHigh Density Grazing will keep grasses vigorous and the severe browsing of re-growth should prevent forest regeneration.

*PHOTOS 18.3 (Chris Burger, Steenbokpan , South Africa) and **18.4** (Elizondo brothers, Tampico, Mexico) show the effects of extremely high Animal Impact on degree of browsing and physical damage of trees. The only explanation for this sort of behaviour by cattle (mainly grazers) is the higher palatability of browse due to the low tannin content of leaf related to time.*

GRASS OR WEEDS GERMINATING

One of the most striking examples I have come across indicating the symbiotic relationship between grazers and grass was where high cattle impact had broken mature surface capping adjacent to a non disturbed area under an electric fence line. At the start of the rains in November there was virtually 100% grass germination on the disturbed area and 100% weed germination where the capping was still intact under the fence line (See Photo 18.7). This clearly shows that severe grazers, in conjunction with the predatory effect (high stock density), enhance the establishment of grassland. Depending on how the hoofs and mouths of cattle are managed, succession will either move toward or away from grassland.

PHOTOS 18.5 and **18.6**: *Stunted grass (left) being grazed and transformed into shoulder-high grass 10 months later (right) – no fertiliser or any other extraneous inputs. Stocking rate was quadrupled in one year. This dramatic change was due to increased soil aeration and soil fertility as well as the stimulation of grass vigour brought about by the mouths and hoofs of cattle managed appropriately. The appropriate management (stock density of 3000 cattle per hectare) is illustrated in Photo 18.5 and the positive consequences of this management can be seen in Photo 18.6.*

PHOTO 18.7: *The beneficial effect of Animal Impact in creating grassland can be seen in this photo taken at the beginning of the rainy season. Grass germinating in the background is the result of a single treatment of high Animal Impact. In the foreground (close to the electric fence) where there was no impact the only plants able to germinate under a mature soil cap (dark surface) are weeds.*

GRASS COLOUR

Probably the most immediate and dramatic change after initiation of high density grazing is the change in grass colour from pale to dark green. An obvious reason for this is a concentration of dung and urine. A less obvious, but very important, reason is soil aeration resulting from soil surface disturbance. The resulting oxidation that occurs, in all probability, makes more nutrients available for plants to assimilate. Soil aeration is of such great importance that it should be emphasised by including it as an ecological process at the same level as water and nutrient cycles, succession (macro succession), energy flow and genotype (micro succession).

THE COMPEXITY AND SIMPLICITY OF NATURE

Unlike the mechanical world where parts can be studied separately and put together to form a whole the opposite applies in the natural world. Here the parts that constitute a whole have to be considered from the perspective of the whole otherwise conclusions and practices will be flawed. Ranchers have to understand that cattle have a dual role – efficiently convert grass into beef and improve the veld on which they graze. **All** management and breeding practices have to conform to these requirements.

The hooves of cattle **can** compact soil and the mouths of cattle **can** result in overgrazing and weakening of plants. The obvious, but erroneous, conclusion **can** be that cattle are intrinsically bad for the veld. **But**, if the role of cattle is understood in the context of a whole comprising severe grazers, grass and the predatory effect then the detail does have relevance. The hoofs and mouths of cattle managed at high stock density, Non-Selective Grazing **and** appropriate time control will result in veld improvement.

Cattle that are efficient at converting grass into beef exhibit good body condition. Inherently good body condition is an essential component of practical fertility as well as nutritional adaptation and drought tolerance. In this context fat is good. However, when we don't understand the whole and focus on the detail then fat is "bad". This is illustrated by the negative correlation between fat (early physiological maturity rate) and growth (ADG) as well as feed conversion efficiency (FCE) in a controlled test over a limited time period (See Chapter 6: MEANWHILE, BACK AT THE RANCH............). When breeders focus on detail without understanding the whole the result is cattle that are **bred to be**

lean and "efficient" and fed to be "productive". Such cattle are genetically handicapped when managed under a regime of high Animal Impact and Non-Selective Grazing in order to fully utilise grazing and improve the veld.

Numerous trials involving grass being defoliated by clipping clearly show a drastic decline in total production as well as root energy reserve at short cutting intervals. Although these results indicate a reduction in grass vigour and yield with shorter intervals between defoliation what about the opposite effect of cattle saliva, soil aeration, dunging and urinating? These factors, constituting a greater whole, aren't considered when using scissors. It is highly probable that the interval required between defoliations for acceptable grass vigour, yield and quality will be shorter in a grazing regime than in a mechanically defoliated regime.

The above examples clearly show that understanding the whole is much more important than understanding detail. Detail has relevance solely within the context of the whole.

With a conventional goal of **maximum production per animal** it is impossible to improve the veld. The focus is narrowed to what will increase individual animal production regardless of the wider consequences. An obvious requirement is to allow animals to graze selectively at a low stocking rate. This leads to veld degradation and a continual downward adjustment of stocking rate. The decline in total production due to fewer animals can only be addressed by increasing production per animal through carrying fewer animals and feeding them with costly external inputs. Furthermore, cows have to be bred to calve out of sync with the seasonal variation in nutrition in order to wean heavier calves. Breeding focuses on increasing the genetic potential for growth (later maturing types) and milk production – nutritionally non adapted genotypes that aggravate the situation. This is the current state of affairs on cattle ranches and is due to man's ego and innate ability to complicate matters.

When we view nature from a different perspective, such as that resulting from an understanding of the grass-grazer-predator relationship as well as a goal of **maximum sustainable profit per hectare**, our relationship with nature is simplified. Our role becomes that of the predator. This is manifested in high Animal Impact and Non-Selective Grazing, production in sync with seasonal variation in nutrition in order to concentrate calving, enhanced natural processes (including rumen supplementation) and accelerated natural selection (survival of the fittest as opposed to the prettiest). The consequences are increased stocking rate (due to improved veld and increased veld utilisation) and more efficient grass conversion (inherently good body condition).

Nature is both complex and simple. When looking at, or working with, detail it is extremely complex and incomprehensible for the human mind. However, when the whole is considered and the focus is on enhancing natural processes management becomes simple. As cattle managers and breeders we should mimic nature. Our role is very simple. We have to play the part of the predator, particularly in grazing management, and we have to accelerate natural selection. This is our part in a much greater whole over which natural forces have jurisdiction. The less we concern ourselves with detail outside these two roles the better.

TIME AND GRAZING

When South African, John Acocks, said "*South Africa is overgrazed and understocked*" he fully understood the time factor in grazing management. Today, more than 50 years after this statement was made, most ranch managers and advisors still do not understand the connection between time and overgrazing. They believe overgrazing to be the result of too many animals.

OVERGRAZING

When a grass plant is severely grazed there is little leaf left for photosynthesis to occur. The only way for new leaf to form, initially, is for energy reserves to be withdrawn from the roots. As the leaf area increases photosynthesis becomes possible and new leaf is formed using energy from the sun. Eventually, when the plant has grown out, root energy reserves are replenished by withdrawal from leaf. Such a plant has recovered from grazing and will remain vigorous if the process is repeated. This process from severe grazing to recovery requires a time interval depending on many circumstances such as species, climate and soil fertility. If a plant is repeatedly grazed because of long term exposure (animals too long in an area or return too quickly) the root energy reserves are depleted and the plant loses vigour resulting in low productivity, a change in species composition and possibly death.

It is important to understand the dynamics of grazed veld, or pasture, with a diversity of plants. Plants, even from the same species, are not equally acceptable to grazers with the result that selection occurs continually. The most palatable plants, speaking in general terms, are the younger ones. If cattle remain in an area long enough for previously grazed plants to have grown sufficiently to be re-grazed they will be grazed in preference to older material due to their greater palatability. The result is selective overgrazing due to too few cattle relative to the amount of grass on offer at that particular time as well as a too low stock density. This is generally the situation on most cattle ranches and is what was observed by John Acocks when he made his famous statement. In other words, under set stocking or inappropriate time control, overgrazing of a percentage of grasses occurs with too few cattle relative to the amount of grass available. There are also a percentage of grasses that are un-grazed and remain so owing to their lowered palatability. Thus, veld in such a situation can be described as being overgrazed and understocked.

OVERRESTING

Under utilised or over rested grass, as in the above situation, is very common with conventional management and results in decreased palatability and vigour and eventually death in very brittle environments. In order for grasses to stay vigorous and palatable they have to be severely grazed at intervals that allow sufficient recovery. This is particularly true of grasses that have evolved with severe grazers and that have growth points close to the ground.

There are very few environments that I am aware of where all grasses are of similar palatability to the extent that utilisation can be even. Most environments have grasses of varying palatability where even utilisation can only occur at high stock density and total utilisation.

PHOTO 18.8: *The effects of simultaneous overgrazing and overresting are very clear in this photo of conventionally managed (conservative stocking rate and selective grazing) tropical sourveld. The patch of severely grazed grass is composed of the same unpalatable species as the surrounding unutilised grass. On returning after a recovery period the same patches will be grazed or left untouched as previously. The solution is to increase both stocking rate and stock density.*

PHOTOS 18.9 (Seasonally humid tropics) 18.10 (Seasonal rainfall arid sub-tropics) illustrate the effects of selective grazing in order to allow high individual animal production. In Photo 18.9 it is also apparent that both palatable (left) and unpalatable species (right) are being overgrazed simultaneously. In the background is an unutilised "unpalatable" grass of the same species that is overgrazed. Photo 18.10 indicates extremely poor utilisation (stocking rate) with only one plant grazed, two unutilised and one dead as a result of overresting. Despite the amount of unutilised grass the rancher in this arid environment was planning to destock due to "drought".

TIME AND TRAMPLING

In southern Africa there is a misconception that the hoofs of livestock compact soil and destroy grasses whilst the hoofs of wildlife, such as buffalo, do not. The hoofs of any hard hoofed animal can either compact or loosen soil depending on stock density and time.

1 X 365 DAYS IS NOT THE SAME AS 365 X 1 DAY

A cow walking between two points daily for a year will definitely compact soil and create a path. However, 365 cows walking between the same two points on a particular day with no further traffic for the rest of the year will have the opposite effect. Instead of a compacted path there will be a wide strip with dark green grass standing taller than the surrounding grass.

TIME AND NUTRITION

QUALITY VERSUS QUANTITY

As can be seen in Figure 18.1 there is an inverse relationship between quantity and quality relative to defoliation interval. The magnitude of the drop in nutritive value also differs between sweetveld (high octane grasses) and sourveld (low octane grasses). On sweetveld it is relatively small and on sourveld it is very high. It is clear from Figure 18.1, which is applicable to sourveld, that the required equivalent daily intake of grass by an animal is four times greater on veld with a long recovery period as opposed to the same veld with a very short recovery period.

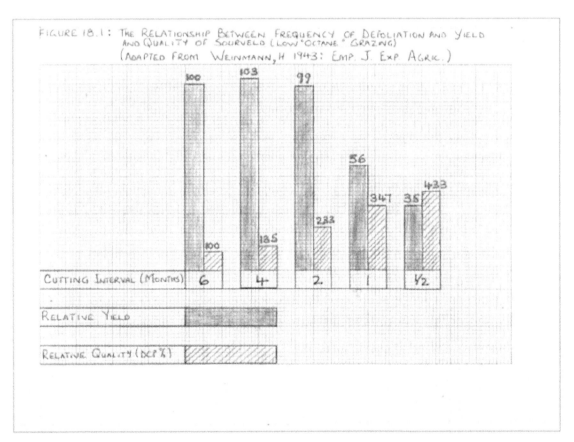

FIGURE 18.1: *THE RELATIONSHIP BETWEEN FREQUENCY OF DEFOLIATION AND YIELD AND QUALITY OF SOURVELD.*

28 X ¼ DAYS IS NOT THE SAME AS 7 X 1 DAY OR 1 X 7 DAYS

When I started UltraHigh Density Grazing on the 12th of January 1995 I realised that under my conditions of tropical sourveld (seasonally high rainfall and low "octane" grasses) I would have to implement sufficiently high stock densities and several moves per day onto fresh grazing in order to achieve a high degree of grass utilisation without the cattle suffering unduly in terms of body condition. An example that substantiated this belief was where one herd of cattle (Herd A) was moved four times in a day and another herd (Herd B) once per day on the same veld. The herd moved once daily was only able to utilise approximately 50% of available grass whilst the herd moved more frequently was able to utilise close to 100% without any visible stress. The problem with herd B was that stock density was t*oo high* (in terms of fouling) *but not high enough* (to counteract fouling and increase grass intake). This principle applies in all environments, but in drier environments with a lower carrying capacity daily moves or moves every few days may not result in the same problem. Frequent moves result in improved utilisation and a lower drop in body condition due to fresh grazing, competition, an even plane of nutrition and stable rumen microbes.

FRESH GRAZING

When cattle move into a new grazing area (paddock) they first scout around and graze the most palatable plants. In time the quality of grazing declines due to fouling (dust, urine and dung) and selection with the result that total nutrient intake/body condition declines. When this period is shortened to hours or a day or so (depending on the environment) this effect is nullified. It is highly probable that intake can actually be increased by frequent moves. This is akin to a feedlot situation where small amounts of feed are put out on demand as opposed to a larger amount weekly. Overall intake will be much greater in the first instance.

COMPETITION

Cattle grazing in close proximity to each other and moved frequently onto fresh grazing are in a highly competitive state in terms of grazing. The result is a voracious grazing behaviour and increased intake.

EVEN PLAIN OF NUTRITION

With frequent moves onto small grazing areas the plain of nutrition stays constant on a daily basis. In some environments the plain of nutrition will be the same at the end of an eight month dry season as it was at the beginning. This must be positive.

RUMEN MICROBES

A constant and appropriate (cellulose digesting) rumen microbe population is essential in order to allow efficient grass digestion (fermentation). Large variations in grazing quality over a period of days must have a negative effect on rumen function whereas the same variation over a period of hours does not.

BUSH/WEED UTILISATION

There is no doubt that frequent moves at very high stock density drastically increase the intake of browse (See Photos 18.3 and 18.4). As discussed previously this is probably due to a decreased tannin content of leaf when time in and out of an area is controlled tightly.

TIME AND ENERGY

Large, intermittent pulses of energy in the form of soil disturbance, root death (after severe grazing), dung and urine have a vastly different effect on the ecosystem as opposed to small, constant doses. This is the situation required by a grassland/savannah ecosystem.

365kg ON 1 DAY IS NOT THE SAME AS 1kg PER DAY FOR 365 DAYS

What would the effect of haphazard, daily applications of 1kg of fertiliser on one hectare of pasture over a period of one year be? Contrast this to the application of 365kg of the same fertiliser on one day on a hectare of well aerated soil when moisture and temperature are ideal for plant growth. The latter situation is similar to that at the start of the wet season in the humid, seasonal rainfall tropics where dry season veld has been grazed at a stock density of 1000 - 3000 cattle per hectare.

TIME AND BURNING

When grazing at sufficient impact it should not be necessary to burn grass. However, in circumstances where fire may be an option (prior to grazing moribund grass in humid environments) or where there has been an accidental burn there are important procedures to follow. A planned burn is best done at the start of the rains in order to limit exposure of soil to sun. As soon as possible after a burn (when grass can physically be grazed) a dose of high Animal Impact (even if created by attractants such as hay and feed cubes) is essential in order to break up surface capping which inhibits soil aeration, water infiltration and the establishment of grass. In certain environments, such as the seasonal rainfall tropics, this capping can be very severe with negative effects on the ecosystem. After this impact and severe grazing, plants require a period of recovery, the length of which will be determined by the environment.

INCREASING VELD UTILISATION

In many parts of the world where ranching occurs the utilisation of grazing is poor. It can be as low as 50% or less. There are several reasons for this. The main one is that, on sourveld (low "octane" grass resulting from high rainfall and poor soil), cattle are conventionally allowed to graze selectively in order to benefit individual performance (goal of maximum production per animal). This is achieved through low stocking rates and low stock densities. The large proportion of grass not grazed exhibits a continual decline in palatability. Even if time is controlled to eliminate overgrazing of the grazed grasses the negative effects of plant selection remain.

PHOTOS 18.11 and **18.12** *show how extremely high stock density can improve the utilisation of sourveld. Photo 18.11 shows an accumulation of moribund grass resulting from conventional management. Conventionally this would be addressed by burning. In this case, however, animal control*

(electric fences) allowed a stock density of 1000 to 3000 cattle per hectare resulting in full grass utilisation (grazing and trampling) as seen in the photo on the right.

STOCK DENSITY

Increasing stocking rate (theoretically possible) in the scenario described, compounds poor animal performance to the extent that animals can die of malnutrition. What is essential is a drastic increase in stock density in conjunction with a higher stocking rate. This has the effect of ameliorating the poorer nutrition (Non-Selective Grazing) as described above – fresh grazing, constant plain of nutrition, competition, rumen function and palatable browse. Appropriate time-control will result in veld improvement and higher quality grazing.

RUMEN FUNCTION

Those of us working with cattle do not really appreciate the miracle taking place on a daily basis. As the case with all ruminants, the microbes in the rumen of cattle allow a large amount of fibrous grass to be converted into an extremely high quality product such as milk and beef. In order for this to be done efficiently the population of cellulose (fibre) fermenting microbes needs to be kept at a high level. Cattle on extremely high fibre (lignified) grazing require assistance from man, in the form of minerals and rumen degradable protein (such as urea) to speed up this process of fermentation resulting in a higher grass intake. There are many sources of information that can assist the ranch manager in achieving the objective of improved rumen function through supplementation in the form of urea and tannin neutralisers such as polyethylene glycol (developed as Browse Plus in Zimbabwe during the early 1990s to assist in browse utilisation). Suffice to say that such an approach is not only cost-effective, but essential, under certain circumstances and in certain environments.

SEEDLING ESTABLISHMENT

How many of us buy expensive grass seed and spread it on compacted soil with a surface cap and expect it to germinate, establish and grow? Wouldn't it be prudent to prepare the soil first by disturbing the surface and fertilising? Yet, we apparently expect miracles to happen on bare ground whether it is large bare patches or widely spaced plants. The conventional approach would be to decrease animal numbers or remove them completely in order for the land to heal.

Cattle have been created with hard hoofs to break up the soil surface so as to aid the establishment and growth of grass. The fact that they can compact soil is due to a lack of the predatory effect. Their hard hoofs only have the desired effect in the presence of time-controlled high Animal Impact.

GRASS VS. WEEDS

There is no clearer indication of the symbiosis between cattle and grass than when grass establishes after time-controlled high Animal Impact as opposed to the predominant establishment of weed where the surface cap has not been disturbed (See Photo 18.7). Similarly, the predominant grasses to establish after soil disturbance are those with round seed as opposed to grasses with awns on their seed. The former grasses are generally more palatable and productive – again indicating the symbiotic relationship that results from the predatory effect.

VIA THE ANIMAL

Generally speaking there is sufficient seed stored in the soil surface for the establishment of grasses and forbs (mainly legumes) after seedbed preparation resulting from high Animal Impact. In time veld can be returned to its climax state. However, with extremely high impact such as occurs when herd effect is created or at constantly high stock density there is a vacuum, so to speak, in terms of available seed and that required to completely cover the ground. This provides an opportunity for introducing extraneous seed of desirable species. This can be done by spreading on the ground or via the animal (mixed with lick supplements) if seed is readily available. This way bare ground can be converted to climax pasture in a very short period of time. This method can also be used to introduce exotic, but valuable, plants such as certain legumes from similar environments without expensive mechanical intervention.

PHOTOS 18.13 and 18.14 show how cattle can be agents of veld improvement via grass seedling establishment. Pictured on the left is ingested seed germinating in a dung pat. Pictured on the right are grass seedlings establishing as the result of sufficient soil surface disturbance due to high Animal Impact.

AERATING THE SOIL

Healthy soil requires aeration – an exchange of air (oxygen) and the compounds of oxidation (carbon dioxide). This process is only effective when soils are porous and the surface is broken, allowing the soil to "breathe". Compacted and capped soils, the result of conventional grazing management, are poorly aerated.

BREAKING THE SOIL SURFACE CAP

There is only one way of efficiently aerating millions of hectares of grassland and savannah in a cost effective manner and that is by disturbing the soil surface with the hoofs of cattle managed under time-controlled high Animal Impact. Not only is the soil aerated, but it is fertilised by dung and urine and plant material is laid down as a cover in order to form humus and feed earthworms and termites that further aerate the soil by creating porous soil.

FEEDING EARTHWORMS, TERMITES AND DUNG BEETLES

It is said that there is more life underground in fertile soil than above ground. This life needs energy and nutrients, much of which originates above ground. Earthworms, in particular, can only feed on plant material that is in the soil or on the soil surface. Dung beetles require dung – the more the better. Such conditions can only occur in the presence of many grazers, such as cattle, managed at high impact.

RELEASE OF NUTRIENTS THROUGH OXIDATION

The importance of soil aeration becomes really apparent after the first dose of high Animal Impact when the colour of grass changes from light green to very dark green. This change in colour can partly be attributed to an even distribution of dung and urine. However, the results are so dramatic that there must be other factors at play. I believe the release of nutrients to plants from a form unavailable to them, through the process of oxidation, to be the major reason for this change in colour and increase in vigour.

PHOTOS 18.15 and 18.16 show the effects that high Animal Impact has on soil life and grass colour. Pictured left is earth worm activity in formerly compacted and surface capped soil (Karoi, Zimbabwe). The photo on the right shows the difference in grass colour due to one treatment of high Animal Impact to the right of the fence in the semi-arid Kalahari of South Africa.

MORE EFFECTIVE RAINFALL

There is a big difference between total rain and effective rain. A total precipitation of 500mm at 90% effectiveness (10% run-off and evaporation) results in more moisture for plants than 1000mm at 30% effectiveness (70% run-off and evaporation). Soil surface conditions, in particular, determine rainfall effectiveness. This is under the control of management.

SOIL SURFACE CULTIVATION

Bare, compacted soil results in very high run-off and evaporation. Breaking up the soil surface with the hoofs of cattle under time-controlled high Animal Impact allows greater water infiltration as well as the formation of a seedbed for the establishment of plants which slow down water flow. This is the only way to decrease water run-off on a large scale.

LITTER

Litter (dung and trampled grass) on the soil surface not only aids water infiltration, but decreases evaporation thus increasing rainfall effectiveness. In humid, or seasonally humid, environments this litter is quickly converted to humus which increases the porosity of soil.

EARTHWORMS AND TERMITES

Burrowing insects and animals create many channels for water to find its way into the soil. These creatures need feed in the form of litter and dead plant roots that must be provided by the appropriate management of the hoofs and mouths of cattle.

INCREASING SOIL FERTILITY

We do not need fertiliser to produce productive pasture. All the ingredients of fertile soil are freely available in the ecosystem. We have to enhance these processes by managing appropriately.

PHOTOS 18.17 and **18.18** show the effect of extremely high Animal Impact (stock density of 3000 cattle per hectare) in laying down dry grass not grazed by cattle. Under conventional management the only practical option to address the problem of moribund grass is to burn it with extremely negative results in terms of soil fertility and rainfall effectiveness – carbon into the air and bare ground. In the situation above, however, litter and evenly distributed dung and urine are incorporated into the soil via decay (by the middle of the wet season in this seasonally humid environment) and insect activity (dung beetles active in Photo 18.18). In a matter of a few years hard, compacted soil can become porous and humus-rich.

PHOTOS 18.19 and *18.20* illustrate the positive effects of trees and legumes in increasing soil fertility. This can partly be seen in the dark green colour of the grass. In photo 18.19 (area rehabilitated from mainly bare ground a few months earlier with herd effect – high stock density and feed cubes used as an attractant) there is a clear correlation between trees and the vigour of grass growing close by. Photo 18.20 illustrates the symbiosis between legume and grass.

RECYCLING VEGETATION

There is a great deal of plant nutrients tied up in plants that remain there until the plant is either grazed and returned to the soil in the form of dung and urine or the plant is trampled and returned to the soil via earthworms, termites and the process of decay. This can also be done by burning, but this is not ideal since carbon, the building block of humus, is lost in smoke. The longer the cycle the less the nutrients that are available for growth. Any grass not grazed during a grazing cycle must be trampled onto the soil surface to eventually be incorporated into the soil for plant use.

OXIDATION TO INCREASE NUTRIENT AVAILABILITY

As mentioned previously, breaking up the soil surface aids aeration resulting in oxidation and the release of nutrients for plants. This, however, is only part of a greater story since much soil life with important functions requires well aerated soil.

NITROGEN FIXATION BY LEGUMES

Legumes are forbs and trees that live in symbiosis with bacteria that are found in root nodules. The host legume provides food for the bacteria and the bacteria extract nitrogen from the air in soil which is used by the host. Legumes are high in protein (produced from the nitrogen). This provides food for grazers and nitrogen compounds (leaf fall and root decay) which are used for plant growth.

TREES

Trees fulfill vital functions in the ecosystem. They create a micro climate that moderates the macro climate in terms of temperature (cooler days and warmer nights) and moisture (less evaporation). Deep rooted trees recycle nutrients from deep underground and deposit them on the soil surface in the form of leaf. This leaf litter also creates humus and limits evaporation. Many trees, particularly in the semi-arid savannahs, are leguminous and increase the nitrogen content of soil apart from providing browsers with protein.

The value of trees in terms of improving soil fertility is apparent to any observer. Grass growing under trees is always darker green than the surrounding grass, particularly on inherently poor soils and in high rainfall areas. Trees are an essential part of the ecosystem in many environments. If they are lacking they need to be planted. If they have been cut down they need to be replaced (See Chapter 21: REPLACING FOREST WITH FUNCTIONAL GRASSLAND).

MORE EFFECTIVE PHOTOSYNTHESIS

All energy originates with the sun. The photosynthetic process in plants whereby solar energy is stored in compounds that can be assimilated directly by man or indirectly after passing through the rumen of animals such as cattle is truly amazing. Cattle ranchers are privileged to be in a position where they can enhance this process through appropriate management.

PHOTOS 18.21 and 18.22 illustrate how Animal Impact has created a very dense cover of grass from bare ground thereby increasing the effectiveness of photosynthesis. The whole area was previously bare ground as indicated by the patch of bare ground in Photo 18.21 which remained under a mineral feed trough where no impact occurred.

PLANT DENSITY

Having more plants per unit of area is the equivalent of a factory with more workers. Time-controlled high Animal Impact that results in greater seedling establishment will increase plant density and solar energy capture.

VIGOROUS PLANTS

Plants with strong root systems and broad leaves will generally be more efficient at photosynthesis. Such plants will be the result of fertile and well aerated soil as well as appropriate time-control. This is a scenario that can be created by the prudent use of the hoofs and mouths of cattle.

19. FROM HUNTER-GATHERER TO MANAGER

CONTROL

Conventional cattle management where cattle are placed in a paddock for a period of time varying from a week or two to forever cannot be described as management. This is more like a hunter- gatherer situation. Management, in terms of grazing, means controlling each hoof and mouth relative to Animal Impact, selectivity of grazing as well as time on and off a piece of land. This sort of control requires that decisions be made on an hourly to daily basis. It also means that there is a penalty for bad decisions and a reward for good decisions. This is the essence of management.

HERDING WITH HERDSMEN

Herding of cattle with herdsmen started with domestication and is still common in many parts of the world. In Africa, in particular, there is a close interaction between humans and cattle. Nowhere is this closer than in areas where cattle and humans are in contact with wildlife such as in East Africa. Here the cattle are dependent on humans for protection against predators. Cattle that have developed under such conditions have an affinity for man and have an inherently strong herd instinct. This makes herding much easier.

I definitely see the potential for herding in tribal situations as well as under commercial conditions such as game ranches where cattle are in close proximity to wildlife. In the latter case the role of cattle is more one of improving the land than efficiently converting grass into beef. This being the case, management misjudgements do not have the same consequences as in a commercial ranching situation where the main, or sole, income is from cattle.

These misjudgements are more likely to occur in the case of large herds where tight bunching (high stock density) is under the control of several herders on foot (as in Africa). A problem under such conditions can be the separation of calves from their mothers. Another problem that is likely to occur is too much competition from the point of view of young stock. The labour requirement for separate herds may be too high. These problems can be eliminated to a large extent with electric fenced paddocks where control is more clinical and the labour requirement lower.

Herding in a commercial situation where stocking rates are low (arid country) and constant herd effect may not be a requirement is probably a very good option. Cattle can be concentrated on specific areas where high impact is a greater requirement (herding and night paddocks) and grazed more loosely elsewhere.

PHOTOS 19.1 and 19.2 illustrate two methods of herding. Pictured on the left is a herd of Boran cattle, with inherent herd instinct, being controlled by a single herdsman. On the right is a herd of Boran crossbred cattle being controlled by a single electrified wire.

PHOTO 19.3: *Management is not possible without control. Illustrated above is the sort of control necessary to enable ranchers to be elevated from hunter-gatherers to managers. This large herd is controlled by portable single strand electrified wires. The wire pictured here controls forward movement and is re-located at intervals throughout the day creating several "paddocks".*

HERDING WITH ELECTRIC FENCES

For the vast majority of ranchers some form of electrified fencing is the answer to the question of cattle control. The main problem preventing the use of these fences is the human mind. Counter arguments range from "they don't work" to "they are too labour-intensive".

Stan Parsons, who had consulting businesses in the USA and Australia, visited my property in 1999. In reference to the labour issue, he said: *"When you realise that the average man to cow ratio in the USA is 1: 250 it is immediately apparent that the Zietsman system is twice as efficient"*. This statement was made on the grounds that at the time I was controlling herds in excess of 500 animals with one man.

Such a low labour requirement is possible with large herds and a semi-permanent fencing system as will be described later. The only limitation to herd size is the amount of water available and the number of animals of a similar class (for example mature cows) that are available to make up a herd. If a business is big enough and the appropriate infrastructure is in place herds of 1000 cattle and more can be managed on a daily basis by one person. This is extremely cost effective in terms of labour utilisation.

To those who refer to electric fences and say "they don't work" I ask the question: "What doesn't work?" Was the wire not insulated? Was the energiser not switched on? Were the cattle not properly trained? Did you not check for power leakages? If your car stops running does that mean that cars can't be used for traveling in? Maybe one should check whether there is fuel in the tank. If there is a broken part then surely it can be fixed. Electric fences are the same. They require attention to detail and maintenance. Those who say they don't work are ignorant or lazy. I believe many are afraid they will work because that means they will have to elevate their management above the comfortable level of hunter-gatherers.

I know of no more cost-effective way of improving the land and increasing ranch profitability than time-controlled high Animal Impact and Non-Selective Grazing made possible by the appropriate use of electric fences. The infrastructure required to treble the stocking rate of my property cost the equivalent of five cull cows. The costs in setting up a semi-permanent system in order to utilise labour more efficiently will be a little higher, but well within the budget of any rancher.

Although I believe that electric fences are the answer to cattle control on ranches there are certain procedures to be followed and pitfalls to be avoided. If this is not done then it is convenient for some to say "they don't work".

ENERGISER

A large output (Joules and distance energised) energiser is essential. The higher cost is justified as there will be fewer problems. What is also essential is that the energiser be well earthed – several rods in the ground and the soil around the rods kept moist. Depending on circumstances, the energiser can be powered via the electricity mains or battery charged by a charger drawing from the mains or a solar panel. Again, depending on circumstances, the energiser can be portable or stationary from where a supply line can deliver a high voltage/low ampere pulse to the energised wire where cattle are being controlled. In the case of a long supply line it is best to have it as part of a permanent fence line (prevents animals not seeing and breaking the supply wire) with the supply wire being low gauge (thicker diameter) and insulated close to the fence poles (off-set insulators are easily damaged by passing animals).

LAY OUT

Ranches vary from intensive to extensive. Climate varies from hot and humid to cool and dry. Topography varies from flat to steep. Cattle may be watered in streams or at a central point with concrete troughs. Numerous factors determine the appropriate stock density, time in an area as well as the time out. All this has a bearing on the required number of paddocks and fencing lay out.

Generally speaking, the most appropriate lay out for most situations is parallel strips created by one or two wires (dry country) with the strips being sub-divided with cross wires. Thus, a strip (portable, semi-permanent or permanent wires) that is 50m wide and 1000m long with cross fences every 50m (portable wire) will create the equivalent of 20 "paddocks". The number of "paddocks" in a 100ha paddock (1000m x 1000m) would amount to 400 (20 x 20). It is these cross fences that allow an extremely high marginal reaction on labour usage as well as capital investment.

Assuming a situation where there is a single water point in the corner of the 100ha paddock, grazing would normally start in the strip closest to water and proceed from strip to strip up to the last strip. Cattle would have access to water along a corridor created along the 1000m boundary of the 100ha paddock. Within each strip cattle are controlled by a front wire, with no back wire, allowing constant access to water (See Figure 19.1). Strip width is determined by the strip length, herd size and the time that each strip is to be occupied.

With one water point strips can be grazed from two sides. With two water points in diagonally opposite corners the paddock can be grazed from all four sides. This spreads the beneficial effect of high impact which is greatest at the entrance to a strip.

There are several variations to the above lay out. The most obvious one is sub-dividing the "spokes" of a wagon wheel with cross fences. Another is strips that are fenced on either side of a stream and away from the stream giving cattle access to water. On steep, but manageable, slopes strips can be created on the contour on either side of a road or corridor that is built diagonally across the slope at a gradient (protected from erosion with ridges) in order to allow cattle access to water.

In intensive situations a completely portable system is possible. This is also the cheapest since the wire, which is an expensive commodity, is on reels and is moved around and used very effectively. In extensive areas where large areas are being managed, a semi-permanent or permanent system is the best option. This will cost more in terms of infrastructure, but the labour requirement will be low. Both the semi-permanent and permanent systems rely on small posts/droppers (approx. 90cm above ground and 25m apart) that are permanently in the ground. In the semi-permanent system the wire is on reels and moved around with the cattle. In the permanent system the wire, creating the strips, is permanently mounted on the posts which adds to cost and should only be a consideration in extremely extensive areas where there is no wildlife that can break fences.

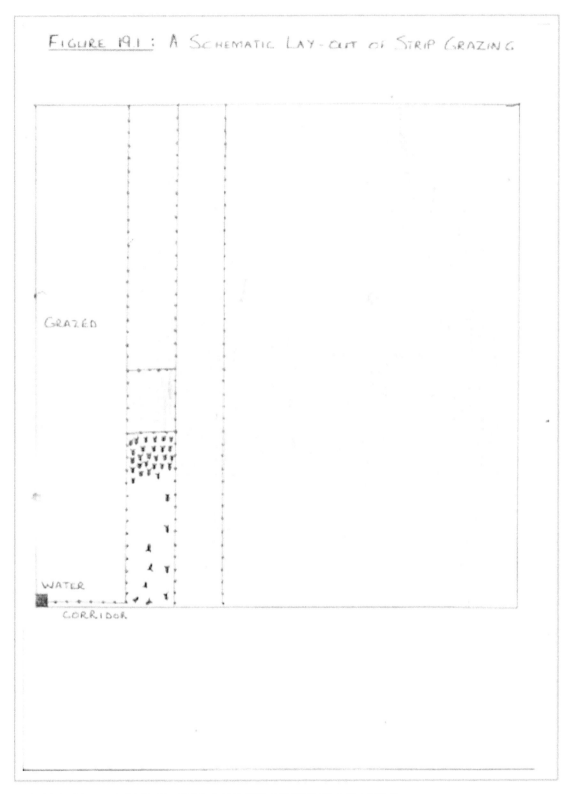

FIGURE 19.1: *A SCHEMATIC LAYOUT OF STRIP GRAZING.*

PHOTOS 19.4 and **19.5**: *Cattle moving down a strip controlled by a cross-wire in front of the cattle and son, Eugene, moving cattle (calling) from the bottom of one strip to the top of the next strip.*

TRAINING

It is imprudent to introduce cattle to small "paddocks" with electrified wire without first alerting them to the fact that these wires shock. If this is not done then the first animal that lumbers into an energised wire across its path will break the fence and create a stampede.

There are several ways of training cattle. One is to erect a single wire fence about 1m on the inside of the perimeter of a small conventionally fenced paddock with water, but little grazing. The more inquisitive cattle will approach the wire and smell it whereby they will be shocked, emit a loud bellow and retreat to the middle of the herd. This will happen a few times and after a day or so the herd will be trained, even without all the animals being shocked – cattle are intelligent and learn from the actions of others.

Another way to train cattle is to immediately introduce them to a strip with a cross fence. This training strip can initially be constructed with three wires that are highly visible (thick gauge wire; broad tape). The cross fence can also be constructed with tape in order to improve visibility and can also be situated so as to increase or decrease stock density. Further down the strip the wires are decreased to two and eventually to only one. I used this method to train a herd of "wild" Nelore (unaccustomed to humans on foot and fleeing from a distance of 300m) in Brazil. After three days they were being controlled by a single wire with posts 25m apart in contrast to the conventional fences consisting of 7 wires and hardwood posts 3m apart. These cattle became so confident that when they saw the herdsman approach the cross fence they would start moving in anticipation of him opening up a new grazing area.

No matter how well trained cattle are, it is important to pay attention to detail. Several times a day the voltage should be checked. There are voltmeters available, but without one the voltage can be checked by touching the wire with a piece of green grass held in the hand. There will always be individual animals that continually test the system with a view to breaking out. That is why it is important to have sub-divisions (conventional paddocks) that can contain animals when they break out. Habitual fence jumpers should be removed from the herd and culled at the earliest opportunity. If this is not done they will teach other cattle bad habits. At times the herd will break out at night (wildlife running through fences) and have full rumens by morning. They will only start grazing later in the day and will still be hungry by late afternoon resulting in another break out at night. The only way to break this cycle is to pen them up securely for a night in order to start their grazing cycle whilst hungry in the morning.

PHOTO 19.6 *shows a herd of "wild" Nelore cattle in Brazil being introduced to a single energised wire (accustomed to 7 strands and hardwood posts 3m apart). The wire seen in the picture is the front wire that is moved at regular intervals. After a day of training it was still necessary to position a herdsman at a short distance ahead of the herd in order to prevent any animal unaware of this wire from blundering into it and causing a stampede. This was no longer necessary after two days.*

PHOTO 19.7: *A herdsman reeling up the front wire and allowing cattle to move into a fresh paddock. Frequent moves at high stock density allow efficient grass utilisation (Non-Selective Grazing) without undue body condition loss.*

GRAZING PROCEDURE

With the appropriate sub-divisions cattle can start grazing a strip closest to water. The stock density can be increased or decreased depending on where the cross fence (portable and independent of the parallel strips) is situated. Stock density can vary between a fraction of a hundred cattle per hectare to 5000 cattle per hectare resulting in a move every day or two to more than 10 moves per day - the equivalent of a few hundred to thousands of paddocks per herd.

Cattle are allowed to graze up the strip and away from water, but with access to water (normally no cross fence behind), until they reach the end of the strip. They then need to walk back down the strip and into the adjoining non grazed strip where the procedure continues. To facilitate the movement from strip to strip the cattle are called each time the cross fence is moved. When they reach the end of a strip the herdsman positions himself at the beginning of the next strip and calls the herd. Eventually the cattle know when they have reached the end of a strip and will move back to the next strip in anticipation of the herdsman moving the cross fence.

The time in a strip depends on herd size relative to strip size. In order to prevent animals staying too long in a strip (overgrazing and overtrampling) herd size may need to be increased and/or strip width decreased.

CATTLE BODY CONDITION

Poor individual animal performance is associated with intensive grazing. This is the result of a decrease in body condition due to poorer nutrition - low selectivity of grazing, in order to improve utilisation and too long recovery periods in some environments. Poorer body condition is exacerbated by the heredity of conventionally bred cattle – bred to be lean and "efficient" and fed to be "productive". It is also exacerbated by timing calving to coincide with maximum weaning weight.

A major flaw in the thinking of many "holistic" managers is the dogmatic abstinence of any form of rumen supplementation and combining different classes of stock into a single, large herd. This has given impetus to the unenlightened sceptics who unconditionally condemn any form of high density grazing.

I entered the realm of Holistic Management *a la* Savory with a very different perspective than the majority of "Holistic Management Educators". My background, as related in the INTRODUCTION (MCV), is that of a theoretical animal scientist and a practising cattle breeder. But there was another difference. I realised we had to implement the ideas of Acocks and Savory in order to improve the land. I also realised we had to do it by considering the other extremely important role cattle have – to efficiently convert grass into beef.

PHOTO 19.8: *The excellent body condition of cows grazing non-selectively at a stocking rate of 1 Large Stock Unit/ha (norm for the area is 1: 4). This rancher (Jaco Prinsloo), from Carletonville in South Africa, was very sensible in actively managing for body condition by feeding a protein supplement during the dry season and by moving constantly(many times a day) onto fresh grazing.*

Now that each animal is under tight control in terms of grazing management, the rancher is obliged to breed and manage for better body condition. A combination of good body condition and high stocking rates will result in maximum sustainable profit/ha. Although explained in greater detail elsewhere, it is opportune to summarise the breeding and management practices that benefit body condition:

-       Separate management of the different classes of breeding stock. Mature cows (from third pregnancy and up), young cows (first and second pregnancies) and heifers must be managed in separate herds and treated differently.

-       Pregnant heifers should be given preferential nutrition (grazing selectively ahead of the mature herd), particularly during the dry season.

-      Rumen supplementation (enhancing a natural process) is **essential** in environments with low "octane" grass.

-      Where rumen supplementation has to be practised, young and pregnant females require much higher levels than mature cows.

-      Calving needs to coincide with adequate nutrition (during the rains for most seasonal rainfall environments).

-      Frequent moves onto fresh grazing.

-      The use of genotypes with inherently good body condition. Generally speaking they are to be found in the "unimproved" category.

CONTROLLING TIME

Time control in respect of plant vigour (herbage yield) and animal nutrition (body condition) will vary between different environments. The emphasis on low "octane "grazing is to benefit body condition (short recovery) whilst on high "octane" grazing it is to benefit plant vigour and ensure drought reserve (long recovery).

PLANT VIGOUR

Grasses in seasonal rainfall areas have to be defoliated at intervals in order to remain vigorous. Both a too short and a too long interval between defoliations will affect vigour negatively. Sufficient time after grazing is required to replenish root energy reserves, replace dead roots and accumulate sufficient leaf for efficient photosynthesis. This recovery period is dependent on factors such as rainfall, temperature, soil fertility, vigour of plants and plant species. The appropriate recovery period in terms of plant vigour will vary from a matter of weeks in hot, humid environments to many months (even years) in arid regions.

ANIMAL NUTRITION

The decline in grass quality (nutrient concentration and digestibility) is rapid and great in fast growth environments (low "octane" grass) but slow and small in slow growth environments (high "octane" grass). Where grasses grow fast and become lignified very quickly management has to shorten recovery periods (even to the detriment of total grass yield) to allow a high daily intake of nutrients in order to benefit body condition. However, there are certain prerequisites that have to be adhered to (See Chapter 20: TIME-CONTROLLED HIGH ANIMAL IMPACT AND NON-SELECTIVE GRAZING).

CONTROLLING ANIMAL IMPACT

Some degree of Animal Impact (dung and urine concentration; soil cultivation; trampling plants; breaking trees and branches) is necessary in all environments and essential in seasonal rainfall environments. There are two reasons why the use of Animal Impact is not common in grazing management. The first reason is that it is perceived to be negative as the case would be if time is not controlled. The second reason is that, up until recently, management was unable to create sufficient impact on a continuous basis over large areas. Another fact to bear in mind is that each environment has a threshold impact below which little change in terms of land improvement occurs.

STOCK DENSITY

Stock density refers to the number of animals on a piece of land at any given time. A stock density of 1000 cattle per hectare does not necessarily refer to 1000 cattle on one hectare since 100 cattle on 1/10th of a hectare would be the equivalent of 1000/ha. Increasing stock density (smaller "paddocks" in practice) has several effects. The first is that selectivity of grazing decreases (utilisation increases).

The second is that there is an increase in the physical disturbance of plants and soil to the extent that individual animal behaviour changes to a point where animals butt each other and physically disturb everything in their path. This behaviour is described as herd effect and can be maintained constantly at high stock densities (approximately 1000 plus).

It is also important to understand that, depending on environment, stock density can be *"too high but not high enough"*. For example, on seasonal rainfall tropical sourveld a situation can be reached where 100 cows on one hectare for one day (conventionally high stock density) would have difficulty utilising available grazing owing to fouling (dung, urine and dust) and would continually move around seeking better grass . However, 100 cows grazing at a density 1000/ha (as opposed to 100/ha) and moved 5 times during the day could fully utilise half the area and be content. The stock density of the first group is too high (in terms of fouling) but not high enough (in order to counteract the effects of fouling.

HERD EFFECT

A situation can arise where it is not possible to maintain constant herd effect. This would typically apply to arid regions with inherently low carrying capacity and severely capped and compacted soils. A good example is the Karoo in South Africa. In such situations stock density must be as high as possible, given the constraints of management, and herd effect created as much as possible. The positive effects of herd effect (over the threshold in terms of impact) in these arid environments remains for several years. It is thus not necessary to achieve constantly high stock density as is the case on tropical sourveld. Stock density that is high enough to eliminate selective grazing and the occasional dose of herd effect should be sufficient for arid environments.

The present situation in areas such as those described above is an accumulated lack of herd effect. The immediate requirement is serious herd effect over a large area. This can be achieved in several ways:

- Wherever possible cattle should be used in preference to sheep as they create greater impact due to their size. A good option, initially at least, would be to buy in cattle, sheep or goats for growing out or fattening in order to create large scale herd effect by a constantly moving "feedlot". Seeding of valuable plants can be done in conjunction with this by broadcasting seed or mixing seed (if cheap and available in large quantities) in the feed or supplement.

- Creating herd effect on specific areas by feeding supplements (hay, cubes or pellets) and confining stock at night on the worst areas. Night paddocks can be created in conjunction with the feeding of bales of hay.

DROUGHT RESERVE

It is important to have a reserve of grazing to bridge the period from the end of one season and the beginning of the following season in a seasonal rainfall area. This could be a few months to many months depending on environment. Without such a reserve a ranch manager grazing intensively could find himself in a situation where all grazing has been depleted with no immediate prospect of rain.

WET ENVIRONMENT

In wet, or relatively wet, environments the greatest gap in fodder flow is between the end of one growing season and the beginning of the next. A reserve of grass is required to cover the period from the end of one growing season (determined largely by rains) and the beginning of the next (worst case scenario in terms of start to rains). This has to be planned.

ARID ENVIRONMENT

Seasonal and long term droughts are a feature of arid environments with erratic rainfall. This requires that managers plan a long drought reserve to cover all eventualities.

MONITORING

Some form of monitoring the change that occurs in both the short and long term is essential. The main reason for this is that we are working with numerous variables that have to be orchestrated in such a way that the outcome is desirable (maximum sustainable profit/ha). As soon as there is any indication of change in the wrong direction **a management (or breeding) decision has to be made**. The sooner this is done and acted upon the better.

GRASS UTILISATION

In order to increase stocking rate, the major determinant of profitability, as much grass and browse as possible must be utilised. There are some parts of the world where all material can be fully utilised just by leaving sufficient animals in a paddock for a long enough period. These are generally dry areas with uniform soils and palatable species. The majority of ranching regions consist of vegetation with variable palatability and acceptability to livestock. In such situations the only option of increasing utilisation is by increasing stock density and enhancing rumen function (rumen supplementation).

SOIL AND PLANT DISTURBANCE

Seasonal rainfall environments require soil and plant disturbance in order for the ecosystem to function effectively. The required degree of impact in terms of severity and frequency will vary between environments. The manager must monitor to ensure that disturbance is sufficient.

PLANT RECOVERY

It is essential that plants remain vigorous. This does not necessarily equate to maximum dry matter yield, particularly in more humid environments. Although regular defoliation, on its own, can result in decreased plant vigour this does not occur in the absence of other positives such as salivation, dung and urine deposition as well as soil aeration and seedling establishment in the presence of hoofs and mouths. So, a degree of overgrazing (technically speaking) may not be detrimental when looking at the bigger picture, especially if grazing is non-selective. Plant recovery time must be considered in the context of nutritive value and sufficient root energy reserve.

NUTRITIVE VALUE

The biggest management mistake in environments with fast growing grasses that mature quickly (low "octane" grazing) is a too long recovery period in the growing season. The consequence of this is what the pioneer African ranchers referred to when they talked of cattle dying of hunger in grass above their shoulders. Unless relatively short recovery periods are planned to benefit the cattle (nutritious grass in the leafy stage), even to the extent of overgrazing (root reserves not fully replenished), their body condition will be unacceptably poor. What this means in practice is that during the fast growth period cattle must return to a previously grazed area whilst palatability, digestibility and nutrient content ("octane" rating) are high and continue doing so until growth is too slow and cattle have to move elsewhere (areas not grazed or only grazed infrequently during the growing season) for the dry season.

Managers must continually monitor grass quality ahead of the cattle. There is not much that can be done about the nutritive value of grass reserved for the dry season other than graze it at high densities in addition to providing cattle with rumen stimulating supplements. There are a few very important provisos. The first is that grazing has to be non-selective in order to prevent undesirable species changes. The second is that areas grazed very intensively during one growing season should not be grazed the following growing season (or only grazed in emergencies) and reserved for the dry season. Another important proviso is to monitor (photos; transects measuring species composition and plant spacing) plant vigour.

PHOTOS 19.9 *and* **19.10**: *Tropical sourveld (low "octane" grazing) at different stages of recovery and with very different nutritional values. The grass on the left has recovered too long and is only useful for grazing during the dry season in conjunction with a protein supplement. During the growing season such grass must be grazed non-selectively and cattle must return (right) before the grass is too rank and of low nutritional value. Intensively and non-intensively grazed areas must be alternated between growing seasons in order to maintain grass vigour.*

PHOTOS 19.11 *and* **19.12**: *High "octane" grass in semi-arid north-western South Africa (the Burger family, Steenbokpan). A relatively low and erratic rainfall necessitates a long recovery period after grazing. Although, at times, severely grazed veld can recover in 2 months or less it is preferable to have a longer recovery period that incorporates a drought reserve. The severity and degree of Animal Impact can be gauged from Photo 19.11. A long and full recovery period as illustrated in Photo 19.12 does not result in too drastic a drop in grass quality in dry environments.*

ROOT ENERGY RESERVE

In arid and semi-arid regions grass quality does not decline to the same extent with time as in humid regions. Here the challenge is to grow more grass and to keep that grass vigorous. Managers need to monitor grass growth during the growing season in order to prevent animals re-grazing grass by remaining too long in a grazing area (strip) and ensure that recovery periods are sufficient. The situation may arise occasionally where rainfall is far in excess of the norm in which case recovery periods may be shortened temporarily for the benefit of the cattle.

BODY CONDITION

Body condition is the A to Z of cattle breeding and management. Small changes in body condition can have large and delayed pregnancy consequences on animal performance. In order to make timely changes in management it is imperative to monitor the precursors of body condition change.

GRASS INTAKE

The utmost importance of a high daily grass intake has been discussed elsewhere. Production only occurs once the daily maintenance requirement has been satisfied. If cattle are still hungry at the end of the day they are losing body condition. A full rumen is at least an indication that the grazing manager (herdsman) has allocated the cattle sufficient grazing during the course of the day. To do so is **essential**. The herdsman has by far the most important role to play in determining the body condition of the cattle under his control. He has to monitor intake and the consistency of dung on a daily basis in order to allow management to make timely decisions in regard to body condition.

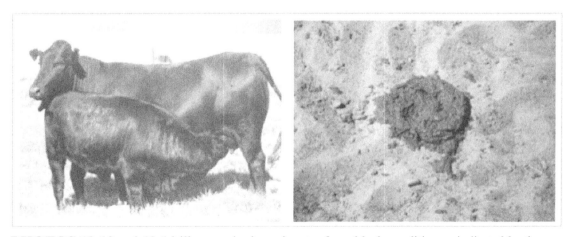

PHOTOS 19.13 and *19.14* *illustrate the determinants of good body condition as indicated by the cow. These are a full rumen and sloppy dung. It is important to monitor these indicators on a daily basis and adapt management where necessary.*

CONSISTENCY OF DUNG

The first observation I make when entering a paddock where cattle are grazing is to look at the consistency of dung. In certain high "octane" grass environments the new growth at the start of the growing season is extremely low in fibre and high in moisture and protein resulting in dung that has no form and is basically liquid – squirting out rather than dropping out. This is not ideal with animals taking on a hungry look with empty rumens. Usually this only lasts a short period and the situation is rectified when the fibre content of grass increases. The only conventional solution is to feed hay. However, with total time control and a planned drought reserve cattle will still be grazing a mixture of new growth and older growth reserved from the previous season resulting in full rumens and better dung consistency (sloppy).

A much more serious problem is dung that has advanced beyond the "French loaf" stage and has become compacted and dry. This indicates lignified grass that the rumen microbes have difficulty fermenting resulting in compaction and a slower passage through the rumen – cattle are suffering an energy shortage and losing body condition. The only solution is to feed the rumen microbes degradable protein (urea is an option) and other nutrients that are essential in order to increase the population of cellulose (fibre) fermenting bacteria. The result is an increased throughput of grass and more energy and other nutrients for the animal. This is reflected in sloppy dung.

BODY CONDITION SCORE

Body condition scoring (1 – 5) does have a place in terms of monitoring long term changes such as those determined by genotype, breeding/calving season and supplementation. For instance, a target body condition score of 3 at calving is ideal in terms of fertility. However, in terms of day-to-day management more sensitive indicators such as rumen fill and consistency of dung are required.

PADDOCK RECORD

It is essential to monitor the overall changes that occur in a paddock or larger grazing area. This does not refer to small grazing strips that may be permanent or changeable depending on the grazing structure.

GRAZING PERIOD

This refers to the period that a paddock (say 50ha consisting of 10 x 5ha strips) is occupied by cattle. There may thus be several sequential grazing periods in a growing season or one in the dry season or one every 15 months in arid country. This recording is necessary in order to monitor recovery times and grazing periods that could have led to serious overgrazing as seen in a decline of stocking rate over time. In such a case time and timing would have to be revised.

GRASS YIELD (CD/ha)

The occupation period of a paddock also has to reflect cattle numbers. For the sake of ease and meaningful recording cattle in this case are synonymous with a **Large Stock Unit** (LSU). A LSU is equivalent to a cow or two suckling calves. A yearling can be considered to be ¾ of an LSU, etc. Therefore, 200 cows plus 190 calves (200 + 95 = 295 Cattle) that graze 45ha for a period of 15 days would equate to (295 x 15/45 = 98) 98 Cattle Days per hectare (CD/ha). One can complicate matters by being more accurate in terms of actual cow size, but as long as one is consistent (a cow is a cow and a calf is a calf) the figures will be meaningful.

STOCKING RATE

Over a period of 12 months a paddock may be grazed several times, once only or not at all (recovery period longer than 12 months in arid environments). However, stocking rate can still be calculated. As an example, consider the case where a paddock has been grazed several times during a 4 month growing season. Four periods of grazing yielded 50, 70, 65 and 40 CD/ha at each grazing resulting in a total of 225 CD/ha. Assuming that this paddock will not be grazed again until the next growing season, which would normally be the case in seasonal rainfall areas, it means that 225 CD/ha is the total production for a year. If the number of days in a year (365) is divided by the total CD/ha (225) the result is the stocking rate which, in this case, is 1.6 ha/LU. A yearly stocking rate record will indicate whether the productivity of a paddock is improving or not.

If a poor year is encountered and all paddocks record a similar relative decline there is no need to change management. But, if one or two paddocks show a negative trend then the reason must be sought and management (time; timing; stock density) adjusted.

CALCULATION AND MONITORING OF DROUGHT RESERVE

In all seasonal rainfall environments it is essential to plan a drought reserve on, at least, an annual basis. This is done at the end of the growing season when no more growth can be expected due to a lack of moisture or heat, depending on environment. In the southern hemisphere seasonal rainfall areas, this is usually at the end of April. There are areas with two distinct rainy seasons in which case the planning needs to be done twice and at the end of each season.

WET SEASONAL RAINFALL

A typical example is the seasonally humid areas of North Zimbabwe and the majority of Zambia. Here the rains normally start mid-November and end mid-March. There are years when the rains can continue into April and, more importantly, there are occasions when the rains only start falling towards the end of December. It is **essential**, in such a situation, to annually calculate the amount of grazing available from the beginning of May until the end of December (worst case scenario) and adjust cattle numbers accordingly.

DRY SEASONAL RAINFALL

A good example is the major cattle ranching areas of Namibia where the seasonal rains can start anytime between December and February and end in March with intervening dry periods. There will be years with very little effective rain. In such a situation it is **essential** to plan a long drought reserve annually from April to April. In other words the amount of grass in April has to carry cattle to the following April. Grass that is grown during this period in most years adds to the drought reserve and will, hopefully, require an upward adjustment of cattle numbers. In such a dry and erratic rainfall environment it is prudent to rely on actual grass available and not on **expected** (hoped for) growth.

CALCULATING AVAILABLE GRASS

At the end of each growing season (normally end-April in the southern hemisphere) it is necessary to calculate the amount of grass (grazing) available. From this figure the number of cattle that can be carried safely (on an annual basis) can be calculated and the stocking rate adjusted. The following steps need to be taken:

1.   Calculate the CD/ha for each paddock.

Some paddocks may have no grass available (grazed intensively during the growing season) whilst others will not have been grazed. The most practical and meaningful way to arrive at a CD/ha figure is to physically graze sample strips in the worst, average and best paddocks (can be part of grazing fire-breaks) and from this calculate the average CD/ha yield for each paddock . For example, in paddock number 3 an experimental strip 100m wide and 1000m long (10ha) was gazed by 200 cattle (200LU) for a period of 4 days. This equates to 80 CD/ha (200x4/10).This calculation is done, or an estimate made, for all paddocks (actual or estimated) in order to arrive at a CD/ha figure for each paddock.

2.   Calculate the CDs for each paddock.

Not only do CD/ha vary for each paddock, but so does the size. Paddock number 3 in the above example is 75ha in size. The CD/ha yield is 80. Therefore, a total of 6000 (80x75) cattle can be carried for 1 day in paddock number 3. This calculation is done for each paddock.

3.   Calculate the total CDs for the property.

This is simply an addition of the CDs for each paddock.

4.   Decide on the length, in days, of the appropriate drought reserve.

In the case of the wet environment it is approximately 240 days (May to December inclusive) and in the very dry environment it is 365 days (May to April) or more.

5.   Calculate the safe stocking rate.

This is done by dividing the total CDs by the length of the drought reserve. For example, in the wet environment example there may be a total of 380,000 CDs that needs to be divided by 240 days giving an actual safe stocking rate of 1583 cattle (380,000/240). If there are currently 1800 cattle it means that the herd has to be destocked by 217 cattle (1800-1583) immediately (every day the action is delayed more cattle have to be removed).

MONITOR

The **estimated** CD/ha figure (just calculated) for each paddock must be reconciled with the **actual** CD/ha figure that is calculated after, or monitored during, the final grazing. If there is a large discrepancy between the two figures it means there is a miscalculation that needs to be addressed in order to maintain a safe stocking rate.

ECOSYSTEM HEALTH

It is essential to institute some form of monitoring to assess how well the ecosystem is functioning. The least that can be done is to have a photographic record of visual change taking place at various fixed points. This will indicate, to a degree, the volume of grass as well as plant species composition and plant density. More meaningful data will be in the form of measurements – species composition, plant spacing, amount of capping and litter in addition to the physical and chemical properties of the soil. The results from this monitoring must be used to assess whether change is desirable. If not, then changes need to be made in management.

PRECURSORS TO ECOSYSTEM HEALTH

It is important to monitor the precursors to ecological change on a constant basis. This means assessing soil and plant conditions on virtually a daily basis in relation to the effect of mouths and hoofs. This enables the manager to manipulate time, Animal Impact and selectivity of grazing in order to achieve the desired effect on the ecosystem function.

- Soil surface disturbance. Sufficient soil surface disturbance is necessary to aerate the soil, increase water infiltration and create a seedbed for the establishment of desirable plant species. The degree of Animal Impact to achieve this will vary according to soil surface conditions - even on the same property.

- Selectivity of grazing. If grasses are grazed selectively, species composition will change negatively. The stock density required for grazing to be non-selective will vary according to soils and species composition. It is necessary to monitor the results of grazing constantly.

- Soil surface litter. The amount of grass litter on the soil surface at the end of the dry season in humid seasonal rainfall areas will determine the rate and degree of humus build-up in the soil. It is important to monitor this during the dry season grazing since there will be no sign of litter in the middle of the wet season in humid environments. In dry environments there may be an accumulation of litter which may require a high dose of Animal Impact (herd effect) to physically break up the litter and accelerate its incorporation into the soil.

- Dung beetles, termites and earthworms. These organisms are essential for increasing soil fertility. Their numbers are dependent on food (dung and grass litter) and the absence of poisons (dips and anthelmintics).

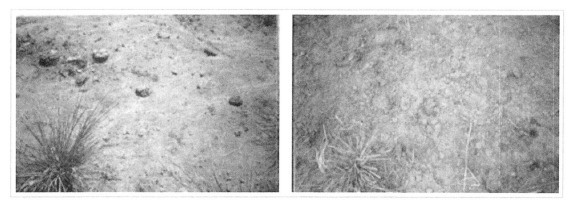

PHOTOS 19.15 and 19.16 are before (left) and after (right) views illustrating the degree of soil surface disturbance required in order to create conditions allowing bare ground to be rehabilitated with grass. The stock density used in this case was approximately 1000 cattle per hectare during the wet season. This single treatment resulted in complete grass cover within a year (Humid seasonal rainfall tropics).

PHOTOS 19.17 and 19.18 are before (left) and after (right) views illustrating the degree of non-selective grazing possible on seasonal rainfall tropical sourveld when grazed at a stock density of 1000 cattle per hectare during the wet season. The same degree of utilisation (grazing and trampling) during the dry season, without undue nutritional stress, would require a stock density of approximately 3000 cattle per hectare.

STOCKING RATE

Stocking rate change indicates the amount of grass produced as well as the degree of utilisation. A negative trend may indicate poor weather conditions and/or inappropriate management.

BEEF PRODUCTION (kg/ha)

Beef produced per hectare is a reflection of weather, management and cattle genotype. Again, the trend may be either negative or positive requiring management and/or breeding changes or affirming appropriate decisions.

PLANT SPECIES COMPOSITION

Changes in plant species is a reflection of short term changes resulting from Animal Impact, selectivity of grazing, time and timing. Because change is seen in the short term (one year in more humid environments and a little longer in drier environments) management can react quickly in order to prevent radically negative results.

PLANT DENSITY

Plant density is not only a reflection of soil type and climate but of Animal Impact also. A decrease in perennial grasses would largely indicate insufficient soil surface disturbance.

GRASS COLOUR

Dark green grass indicates good soil aeration and efficient water and nutrient cycles. The precursor to this is Animal Impact.

SOIL STRUCTURE AND SOIL FERTILITY

This is the ultimate test of ecosystem health and a reflection of all management practices. Accurate monitoring would require physical and chemical analysis of soil.

*PHOTOS **19.19** and **19.20** were taken at the same monitoring site a year apart in the middle of the wet season. Even a casual observance indicates a massive change in both species and mass of grass after two treatments of high Animal Impact and Non-Selective Grazing. Physical monitoring showed a decrease in unpalatable species (Sporobolus pyramidalis) from 86.0% down to 46.0%. Highly palatable species (predominantly Urochloa spp.) increased from 4.5% to 26.0%. The spacing between perennial grass plants decreased (greater plant density) from 9.0 cm to 5.6 cm. The proportion of young perennial plants (seedlings) increased from 0% (40.0% plants moribund; 26.0% plants dead) to 78.0%. The precursors to this change were altered soil surface conditions and accelerated recycling of pant material. The fast rate of change was due to high seasonal humidity (1000mm of rain from mid-November to mid-March).*

*PHOTOS **19.21** and **19.22** underline the importance of monitoring. The progress made after one year in terms of species change, as discussed under Photos 19.19 and 19.20, was reversed from 26.0% (Photo19.21) to10.0% palatable species after two years (Photo 19.22). The reason for this was selective grazing over a large area during the growing season. This management practice was changed to Non-Selective Grazing at shorter intervals over a smaller area, with positive results.*

20. TIME-CONTROLLED HIGH ANIMAL IMPACT AND NON-SELECTIVE GRAZING

In the foregoing chapters the basic principles of high Animal Impact and Non-Selective Grazing were discussed. In this chapter the specifics in terms of time, timing and stock density as it applies in varying environments will be discussed. This is not intended to be a recipe, but a guideline. The reader must understand that the manager on the ground is the one who pulls the strings. The outcome is dependent on how well the "orchestra" (grass and grazers) is conducted. Apart from grazing management this involves harmonising genotype, rumen function and production relative to seasonal variation in nutritional level. Managers need to be decisive. It is inevitable to make mistakes. These can be corrected quickly and minimised with the appropriate monitoring. This is the only way to make progress.

It is worth repeating some truths. The number of animals carried on a piece of land has a far greater influence on ranch profitability than individual animal production. But, a combination of high stocking rate and optimum performance as reflected in fertility (body condition) results in maximum profit/ha. A problem encountered by the majority of ranchers practising UltraHigh Density Grazing is insufficient animals, particularly where the utilisation of low "octane" grazing has been increased. The dilemma is then one of decreased overall production and profit and too much grass – there are insufficient cattle to compensate for the drop in individual production. If it is possible to match cattle numbers to the available grass then overall production and profit will increase. If, in addition to more cattle, these cattle can perform optimally (body condition) owing to the appropriate genotype and calving season as well as optimum rumen function then production and profit will increase in line with an increase in cattle numbers.

It is time everyone considered the bigger picture and measured productivity in terms of **maximum sustainable profit/ha** instead of **absolute individual performance**. Rather than solely looking at calving rate, which is largely a function of nutrition (number of animals on a piece of land), look at the total number of calves born on a property. Rather than considering individual weaning weights consider the total weight of all calves weaned on a property. Rather than looking at total production, look at total profit and return on investment (See Chapter 6: MEANWHILE, BACK AT THE RANCH............).

HUMID, SEASONAL RAINFALL TROPICS

The humid, seasonal rainfall tropics (approximately 800 – 2500mm rain in 4 – 8 months) pose the greatest challenge and at the same time offer the greatest opportunity to the rancher. The climatic factors that pose the challenges are the same factors that offer the opportunities (See Chapter 21: REPLACING

FOREST WITH FUNCTIONAL RANCHLAND). This environment is the last frontier in terms of cattle production.

STOCK DENSITY

Owing to the mass of grass and its low "octane" rating it is essential to maintain a high stock density (necessitating frequent moves) in order to achieve sufficient utilisation and acceptable intake. The required average stock density will vary between 1000 and 3000 cattle per hectare, depending on the season. Apart from the mentioned benefits, this degree of Animal Impact will also ensure an effectively functioning ecosystem by aerating the soil and laying down unutilised grass.

RECOVERY PERIOD

Grass growth is extremely fast during the active growing period resulting in a rapid decline in digestibility and overall quality. This fast seasonal grass growth is superfluous to cattle requirements, at a constant stocking rate, during the growing season resulting in an accumulation of grass. This accumulated grass, essential for the dry season, can be managed in two ways. The first option is to graze cattle at a high density and move them fast allowing selective grazing and sufficient recovery time for the grazed grasses to fully restore root energy reserves. Dry season reserve will predominantly be unutilised grass. The second option is to implement "planned overgrazing". This entails Non-Selective Grazing with short recovery periods, even to the extent of overgrazing, in order to ensure quality grazing. This means that a portion of an area will be intensively grazed during the growing period and on the other portion the grass will be stockpiled for dry season use. These intensively grazed and non-grazed areas should be alternated between seasons in order to maintain sufficient root energy reserves.

Of the two options, "planned overgrazing" is by far the best in terms of both cattle body condition and grass species composition. The benefits in terms of body condition are obvious. Although grasses are temporarily overgrazed this is done non-selectively resulting in a predominance of the more palatable grasses which appear to recover quicker under high Animal Impact. The problem with the selective grazing option is rapid change in grass composition favouring the less palatable, fibrous grasses without a clear benefit to the cattle.

DROUGHT RESERVE

Even though rainfall is high and generally reliable, a drought reserve is essential for several reasons. Firstly, a late start to the rains can cause a major problem when land is fully stocked and veld fully utilised. Secondly, initial growth that starts mainly from root reserves is nutritious and low in fibre and can result in temporary scouring. New growth mixed with mature material eliminates this possibility. Thirdly, there may be a need to use a hot fire to control excessive bush.

Such a need may arise in the initial stages of UltraHigh Density Grazing when insufficient cattle numbers prevent the use of animal impact to control bush. A fourth reason could be to stockpile grass over and above that required for the cattle in the event of an unplanned fire as often happens in Central Africa. If possible, such a reserve should be in areas that may require a burn. In the event of no unplanned fire and no use of the stockpiled grass for grazing it can be deliberately burnt in order to control bush.

Depending on the length of the dry season a small or very large reserve will be required. In most years there will be sufficient rain and fresh grass growth before the drought reserve has been grazed. In such cases it would be prudent to move the cattle quickly through this area at very high stock density in order to trample the grass onto the ground. This material, when on the soil surface, will decay rapidly (a month or two) under the prevailing conditions of high humidity and insect and microbial activity. If this process cannot be finished in time (new growth must be grazed before it matures) then an option would be to burn with a "cold" fire – after rain, at night or early morning – to retain as much litter on the ground as possible.

SEMI-HUMID, SEASONAL RAINFALL TROPICS

The semi-humid seasonal rainfall tropics (approximately 500 – 800mm of rain in 4 – 6 months) generally produce better quality grazing than the humid tropics. However, there are areas with poor soil fertility that produce low "octane" grass even under conditions of relatively low rainfall. An area that comes to mind is the granitic sandveld along, and to the south of, the central watershed in Zimbabwe. In terms of recovery period after grazing the same procedure should be followed as in the humid tropics.

STOCK DENSITY

The need for a high stock density in this environment is similar to that required in a more humid area. However, there is probably a greater need for it here in terms of addressing soil capping and compaction. Generally speaking, the required stock density will be in the range of 500 to 3000 cattle per hectare in well grassed areas. Areas with sparser grass will have to maintain sufficient stock density (a few hundred cattle per hectare) in order to fully utilise grass whilst creating herd effect (night paddocks; bales of hay; supplement feeding; attractant) on areas requiring it.

RECOVERY PERIOD

In general, recovery periods in the growing season will be in the region of a month or two and will be biased towards individual animal performance (body condition). However, there will be situations (as mentioned above) where recovery periods will have to be shorter in order to allow cattle to attain optimum body condition. Whatever the specific environmental conditions, grazing should be non-selective so as to prevent undesirable changes in veld composition.

DROUGHT RESERVE

Sufficient drought reserve is critical, particularly in view of the fact that rainfall is less reliable than in the humid tropics. Considering that the climax vegetation in this region is predominantly woodland and savannah, it may be prudent to include a fire reserve that in most years can be used for a planned burn and in an emergency to feed cattle.

SEMI-ARID, SEASONAL RAINFALL SUB-TROPICS

This environment receives, on average, less than 500mm of rain in under 6 months and is what would generally be termed "good cattle country". Not only is the "octane" rating of the grass high during the growing season, but this high nutritional status is maintained throughout the dry season. The challenge here is quantity and not quality. Nutritionally non adapted cattle under conventional grazing management are able to perform well. However, the issue of nutritional adaptation will have to be addressed when cattle are subjected to Non-Selective Grazing, particularly in areas such as the Kalahari sandveld of South Africa, Botswana and Namibia where there is considerable variation in grass species palatability.

STOCK DENSITY

There are areas with fertile soil where the various grasses are of similarly high palatability enabling a high degree of utilisation by cattle at relatively low stock density (less than 100 cattle per hectare). But, there are also areas, as mentioned, with varying grass palatability where stock density needs to be much higher in order to increase veld utilisation. In such areas stock density needs to be higher than 100 cattle per hectare. There are also many instances where Animal Impact needs to be much higher than can be achieved at the stock density enabling total grass utilisation. In these instances herd effect will have to be created.

RECOVERY PERIOD

In this dry environment with an unreliable rainfall and dry periods within the rainy season recovery periods must be much longer in order to allow grasses to recover fully after severe grazing in addition to catering for within season dry spells. The decline in quality that may occur in certain environments, such as the eastern Kalahari, should be addressed via cattle genotype and rumen supplements rather than a short recovery period and/or selective grazing. During the occasional wet year an exception may need to be made in order to boost the body condition of lactating cows.

DROUGHT RESERVE

In extremely dry, sweet (very high "octane" grazing) areas the recovery period should be long enough to cater for both grass recovery and sufficient drought reserve. This can be in the region of 15 months. In less arid country a drought reserve of 12 months may suffice with the proviso that paddocks are grazed at different times over a period of years. Where there is insufficient control of time due to a lack of infrastructure (insufficient paddocks) an area can be divided into three sub-divisions – A, B and C. Area A is grazed for a period of 6 months with as much time-control and animal impact (internal paddocks) as possible. This is followed by Area B for a 6 month period and finally Area C for 6 months before the cycle is repeated. This should ensure sufficient recovery of grasses, even with occasional overgrazing. Also, it will be obvious if stocking rate is not in line with available grazing – either cattle will need to be moved before the 6 month period is over or too much grass will remain after the allocated 6 month grazing period.

WET SUMMER, COLD DRY SEASON

The eastern Highveld (over 1300m above sea level with 600 – 1000mm of rain falling in 6 months) region of South Africa falls into this classification. Although not typical "cattle country", this is where most of the cattle in South Africa are concentrated. Summer grazing is generally of good quality allowing good weight gains. Winter grazing is frosted and of poor quality. With appropriate grazing management and legume reinforcement the potential stocking rate is 1 LU/ha.

STOCK DENSITY

Generally speaking, stock density will be dictated more by a requirement for efficient veld utilisation rather than Animal Impact *per se* since overall plant density is very high. An exception will be areas that have been invaded by perennial weeds such as *slangbos/bankrtotbos* where herd effect will be necessary to reclaim grassland. The required stock density will vary in accordance with grass palatability and veld composition. Areas with fertile soils and palatable grasses such as rooigras (*Themeda triandra*) can be satisfactorily utilised at stock densities of around 100 cattle per hectare whilst other areas (mainly *Eragrostis spp.*) require densities in excess of 500 cattle per hectare.

RECOVERY PERIOD

Recovery periods will have to be planned in order to benefit cattle rather than maximum grass production. Grazing must be non-selective and areas that are intensively grazed during summer must alternate with areas not grazed or less severely grazed.

DROUGHT RESERVE

All areas must have an appropriately planned annual drought reserve starting from May. In the eastern region this should last until the end of November and in the western region up until the end of December.

ARID

Arid regions probably have the highest redeemable productivity when one considers the extent of degradation. An example is the Karoo region of South Africa which once supported a very large population of wildlife including migratory herds of millions of springbok. Rivers that once teemed with fish and were home to large herbivores such as hippo are now dongas channelling flood water to the sea. The worst cases of water erosion are to be found in these arid regions – floods and droughts alternate within a matter of months. Man will initially have to make extra effort in the form of herd effect to start the rehabilitation of these areas.

STOCK DENSITY

Owing to the extensiveness and low carrying capacity of the region it is difficult to achieve high enough stock density to create constant herd effect (total plant and soil disturbance). This, however, does not abrogate modern man from his responsibility to restore the environment to its full potential.

It definitely did not prevent an enterprising man by the name of Andre Lund of Beaufort West from devising a practical means of creating constant herd effect with a combined herd of sheep, goats and cattle (See Chapter 22: SEEING IS BELIEVING). What Andre has pioneered may seem too drastic to some. What about a herd of 100 million springbok "devastating" everything in its path? This is the only alternative.

It is worth noting that the positive effects of herd effect remain for a considerable time (several years?) after the event. Sufficiently high stock density in order to create overall herd effect will have to be created at intervals. In the intervening period stock density will have to be high enough to avoid selective grazing with herd effect created (night paddocks; feeding attractant) where necessary.

RECOVERY PERIOD

A feature of this environment is the paucity of rain and uncertainty of when it falls. At times plant growth is limited by moisture and at other times it is limited by temperature or both. The result is that recovery periods have to be long – much, much longer than the six weeks advocated during the early years of Non-Selective Grazing (Acocks) and Short Duration Grazing (Savory).

DROUGHT RESERVE

It seems prudent to extend a long recovery period into a drought reserve. This could be anything over a year, depending on the environment. If long recovery periods required for plants to recover result in poorer quality grazing then this issue has to be addressed by providing rumen stimulating supplements, regular moves onto fresh grazing as well as breeding genotypes with inherently good body condition.

21. REPLACING FOREST WITH SUSTAINABLE RANCHLAND

As mentioned earlier, the last frontier for the horizontal expansion of cattle production is the humid and semi-humid tropical forest and woodland of Latin America and Central Africa. Development will inevitably occur, whether we like it or not, owing to the rising demand for food in a world with a rapidly increasing population. There is absolutely no doubt about the fact that, in general, the man-made ecosystem currently replacing the original ecosystem is **unsustainable**. But, this does not mean that cattle are the culprit. The culprit is man. The solution is to encourage, or force, ranchers to re-arrange the components of an ecologically effective, but not necessarily economically productive, ecosystem into one that is managed in an ecologically and economically sustainable manner. This means creating an agricultural system that mimics nature.

PHOTOS 21.1 *and* **21.2**: *Forest being opened for ranching in the Chaco region of Paraguay. The unsuitability for ranching in the natural state can be gauged by the dense forest on either side of an access road (Photo 21.1). Photo 21.2 shows forest opened up in accordance with an environmentally approved plan and with large blocks of planted pasture. Although some forest remains in its natural state the resulting ecosystem of predominantly monoculture pasture is not sustainable.*

PHOTOS 21.3 and **21.4**: *The man-made pasture (Chaco) of scattered trees and planted African grass (Panicum maximum) as shown in Photo 21.3 is not sustainable. It requires many more trees and a greater diversity of grasses and legumes. Photo 21.4, taken in the seasonal rainfall tropics of central Africa (Karoi, Zimbabwe), shows an ecosystem with a diversity of plants (trees, grasses and legumes) resulting from the actions of severe grazing and browsing wildlife in the past. This is what ranchers have to mimic in order to attain sustainability.*

The naturally occurring vegetation in the humid and semi-humid tropics is thick forest or woodland with an understory of sparse forbs and grass. In such a situation the carrying capacity, from a cattle point of view, is extremely low. Also, the grasses that do grow here naturally are generally of poor quality. Some of the timber is very valuable, but much of it is used as firewood or charcoal. Although such forest is, from an ecological point of view, vital it does not detract from the fact that man, in general, sees it differently. Some will exploit its valuable timber without any regard to the consequences. Others will deforest and plant crops such as soya beans for which there is currently a high demand and good price. Others will deforest and plant mainly monoculture pastures for cattle. None of these agricultural practices are sustainable because the man-made ecosystem is not functioning effectively.

Some extremely important facts about this environment have to be understood. The rainfall is largely seasonal (4 to 8 months) and heavy, varying between approximately 800mm and 2500mm. Large areas have soil of inherently low fertility. An overwhelming proportion of the nutrients in the ecosystem are tied up in vegetation as opposed to the soil where it is rapidly leached. Without deep-rooted trees that re-cycle soil nutrients massive leaching occurs resulting in a rapid drop in soil fertility. A good grass cover does protect the soil, but cannot prevent soil fertility loss due to leaching.

Wherever tropical forest and woodland are to be converted to agriculture the following needs to be heeded:

- A certain portion of the land must remain in its original state.

It goes without saying that that these tropical forests have a vital function in the health of our planet by capturing carbon dioxide and releasing oxygen. They are also home to numerous plants with potentially beneficial properties for mankind. These plants, together with the animals they support, must be preserved.

The portions of forest left intact need to be large enough to be self perpetuating. This is in addition to rough terrain and riverine areas that should be left untouched. There will obviously be wide ranging views as to what is large enough, depending on which side of the fence people find themselves. However, there are accepted guidelines that can be followed such as those currently legislated for the Chaco area of Paraguay as well as Brazil.

- Areas that are cleared for agriculture must be developed in a way that mimics, or is an improvement on, the original ecosystem.

This means, in particular, that the nutrient cycle is maintained or improved upon. It is essential that rows of relatively closely spaced large trees be the foundation of an effective nutrient cycle by limiting leaching (re-cycling nutrients leached from the topsoil) and adding nutrients in the form of nitrogenous compounds (leguminous). These trees must be a permanent part of the landscape.

For example, if cropping is alternated with pasture for cattle then the trees must remain and only the area between the rows of these permanent trees (20m wide?) should be cultivated. During the pasture phase smaller leguminous trees can be planted in narrow rows (2m wide?) between the permanent trees together with an appropriate variety of grasses and compatible legumes.

PHOTOS 21.5 and **21.6**: *Deep rooted leguminous trees being used to enhance soil fertility in the seasonal rainfall tropics. Illustrated in Photo 21.5 is a row of Faidherbia albida (Zambia) with annual crops growing on either side. This particular tree has no leaf during the wet season thus allowing other plants growing close to it full access to sunlight. The leaf fall fertilises the soil and benefits the accompanying crops or pasture. Photo 21.6 is of a seed plantation of shorter growing Leucaena leucocephela in the Chaco region of Paraguay. When planted in narrow rows in combination with Panicum maximum grass the carrying capacity of pasture was doubled.*

Although more work needs to be done in identifying appropriate trees, legumes and grasses for the different areas there is sufficient knowledge and common sense around for a start to be made. *Fiadherbia albida* (formerly *Acacia albida*) is a very large leguminous tree found on the flood plains of African rivers and used for alley cropping. Apart from being efficient at fixing nitrogen from the air and producing nutritious pods that are relished by most animals it has the added advantage of losing its leaf during the wet season and growing a thick canopy during the dry season. The significance of this is that crops that are grown during the wet season are not shaded and benefit full sunlight.

Another tall growing tree that is leguminous is *Acacia polyacantha* which occurs naturally in tropical Africa and Asia. It adds a great deal of nitrogen to the soil from leaf fall, but its big advantage is that it establishes easily and grows very fast, even in competition with tall growing grass (acts as a pioneer tree on fallow cropland or disturbed areas). Smaller leguminous trees that should be grown in between the rows of large trees such as *Faidherbia albida* and *Acacia polyacantha* are the different *Leucaena spp.* from tropical Central and South America as well as *Dichrostachys cineria subsp. nyassana* (less thorns) and the shorter lived *Sesbania spp.* from Africa and Asia. Grasses that can be grown, depending on rainfall and soil type, are the different *Panicum spp.* (particularly *Panicum maximum*), Rhodes grass (*Chloris gayanus*), *Brachiaria spp.* and, in drier country, Buffel grass (*Cenchrus ciliaris*).

Twining legumes that can be grown in conjunction with the grasses are *Desmodim spp.* (*D. uncinatum*, *D. intortum* and *D. subsericeum*), *Siratro (Macroptilium atropurpureum)* and *Neonotonia wightii*. In drier country the different *Stylosanthes spp.* (Graham, Seca, Amiga, Fitzroy, etc.) can also be combined with the tropical grasses. For more detail, visit www.tropicalforages.info.

- All management practices must enhance natural processes.

Whether growing crops or raising livestock, management practices must enhance all the natural processes. Grazing management must be on the lines recommended for the seasonal rainfall, humid tropics. Although much progress has been made in terms of minimum till and no-till, it is doubtful whether cropping can be truly sustainable without the integration of pasture leys and livestock, particularly where two crops are grown in a year. In both the cattle and pasture phases the use of chemicals must, at least, be reduced drastically.

If we knew what damage chemical (poison) intervention was doing to our health and the general health of the ecosystem we would be shocked into finding alternative measures. An example mentioned previously comes to mind. In a herd of cattle on tropical sourveld the amount of dip used was decreased by hand-spraying around the neck and head area a small amount (5ml) of pour-on dip (supposedly environmentally friendly) was applied to the tail root. For a period of 4 days after this was done all dung beetles were killed owing to dung contamination – apparent due to observing cattle grazing at ultrahigh stock density.

I have absolutely no doubt that there are currently cattle genotypes available that only require a minimum of chemical inputs (dip) in the tropics. I am also convinced that with the appropriate selection (tick count; body condition) and the appropriate management (body condition; immune function) it will be possible to raise cattle without dips and drenches. I make this statement on the basis of personal experience.

22. SEEING IS BELIEVING

Although high density grazing has the potential to dramatically increase (at least a doubling under most circumstances) the stocking rate of ranches there are very few managers practising it. The reason for this is varied –mainly lack of confidence, inappropriate goal and "too hard work". The majority who have implemented it successfully fall into the category of those who "don't know what they can't do".

Without exception all want to improve their land. Some have experienced poorer individual animal performance (genotype; management) and are working on rectifying it. The vast majority, if not all, recognise the benefits and would not contemplate a return to conventional management. The following short synopsis is to give recognition to some of the few who have gone through the "sound barrier", so to speak, as well as to motivate the rest.

KAROI, ZIMBABWE

I initiated Ultrahigh Density Grazing on the 12th of January, 1995. Capital investment in infrastructure amounted to the equivalent sale value of 5 cull cows. Stocking rate was doubled within a few weeks, in the driest year (375 mm; average is 800 – 1000 mm), due to improved utilisation of conventionally grazed tropical sourveld. Two years later stocking rate was treble the accepted norm. When I was forced off my land in 2002 it would have been possible to quadruple stocking rate. Without a conventionally managed control it is difficult to accurately quantify any change in individual animal performance. I estimate an approximately 10% drop in the individual production of conventionally bred cattle at treble stocking. This could have been eliminated, or improved on, in time with a superior genotype (Veldmaster) and improved rumen stimulating nutrition.

PHOTOS 22.1 and **22.2:** *Pictured in the left photo is a cow and calf illustrating the general body condition of cattle a year after grazing non-selectively at double stocking rate in the driest year on record (375 mm). The photo was taken in the 1996 wet season when rainfall returned to average (1000mm). The right hand photo is of a 14-year-old Giant Rhodes grass/tropical legume pasture that carried 1.25 Large Stock Units per hectare without any fertiliser. The productivity of this pasture could have been improved with the inclusion of leguminous trees.*

*PHOTO 22.3 and **22.4** showing dry season impact and non-selectivity of grazing (left) as well as an extremely high stock density of 5000 cattle per hectare (right) used as a "once-off" in order to trample a moribund patch of grass.*

*PHOTOS 22.5 and **22.6**: The application and result of herd effect on my brother, Wessel's, property. Seen on the left is a herd of weaned calves being fed milled maize stover on bare, compacted ground during the dry season. The feed troughs were moved twice daily in order to cover a larger area. The positive results of herd effect can be seen in the photo on the right where formerly bare ground was covered in a mixture of pioneer and climax grass species two months into the wet season.*

*PHOTOS 22.7 and **22.8**: The beneficial effect of trees on grass growth can be seen in these two photos. In the photo on the left the dark green colour of grass under the tree in a wet year (1300 mm in 4*

months) is evidence of higher soil fertility (leguminous tree and efficient nutrient cycle). Cattle can be seen disappearing in grass growing near trees in the photo on the right.

PHOTOS 22.9 *and* **22.10** *illustrate the response of vigorous grass to rain. On the left certain grasses have seeded after only 64 mm of rain. On the right all grasses have seeded a month later and with a total of 200 mm of rain. Interestingly the most palatable species recovered the quickest.*

BEEFCOR, PRETORIA, SOUTH AFRICA

The management of Beefcor near Pretoria in South Africa are world leaders in terms of the scale with which they have implemented Ultrahigh Density Grazing. For the past 9 years they have been able to background a total of between 30,000 and 40,000 calves (groups of calves spend 3 – 4 months on grass plus supplement varying between 2 – 4 kg per animal per day) per year on 1500 ha of predominantly veld grazing.

PHOTOS 22.11 *and* **22.12:** *The utilisation of sourveld by calves being backgrounded by Beefcor, Pretoria. The photo on the left shows a wide strip being grazed in order to form a firebreak. Photo 22.12 illustrates the impact required on sourveld as well as calves moving into a new "paddock".*

STEENBOKPAN, SOUTH AFRICA

Johan and Hester Burger, together with sons Chris and Niel, were initially involved in managing two game ranches which they own in the semi-arid Steenbokpan area of South Africa close to the Botswana border. It did not take them long to realise that game confined by fences and in the absence of pack hunting predators led to veld degradation. They realised that to improve the veld they would have to use cattle and manage them in lieu of large herds of severe grazers and predators. They moved cattle onto one of their properties where Chris controlled them with portable electric fences. Five years down the line they are carrying between 3 and 4 times the number of cattle (depending on season) that is the norm for their area. The Burgers (Johan is an Engineer by profession) are a prime example of not knowing what can't be done. If it makes sense they will find a way of doing it. Chris deserves credit for his perseverance in operating electric fences in order to control cattle under difficult conditions – free moving game, predators, dry soil (poor conductivity) and bush. They are also in the process of breeding a Veldmaster herd.

PHOTO 22.13: *A promising young Veldmaster bull bred by the Burgers. His dam calved at 2 + 3 years of age under conditions of high Animal Impact and Non-Selective Grazing at treble to quadruple the recommended stocking rate. In time they plan to have a single breeding season of 42 days which will expedite their A.I. programme. This is currently not possible due to the fact that they have had to bring in cattle that ran under different management regimes.*

PHOTOS 22.14 *and* **22.15**: *These two photos clearly illustrate the impact possible with cattle and the clinical precision with which it can be done when using electric fencing. They also show the degree of grass and bush utilisation occurring – a major contributing factor to the Burger's high stocking rate.*

BURGERSDORP, SOUTH AFRICA

Dupie and Lana du Plessis who live in the cold mountainous area between Burgersdorp and Jamestown in South Africa are a husband and wife team who should be commended and recognised for their efforts in managing land in an ecologically and economically sustainable manner. Managing cattle and sheep, controlled by electric fences they erect themselves, on a 600ha property they were able to double stocking rate. They were also able to pay off the property in a relatively short period of time. This is no mean feat.

PHOTOS 22.16 and *22.17*: *The du Plessis property in the high mountains in the Eastern Cape Province of South Africa where temperatures can drop to minus 20 degrees Celsius in winter. In Photo 22.16 cattle and sheep are shown running together under the control of two energised wires. The degree of utilisation possible on this veld with a mixture of palatable and unpalatable grasses is apparent in Photo 22.17.*

BEAUFORT WEST, SOUTH AFRICA

Andre and Martie Lund from Beaufort West in the Western Cape Province of South Africa are pioneers in the field of veld management in the arid Karoo. Initially they were involved with John Acocks in the 1960s and to a degree with Allan Savory and Stan Parsons in the 1970s. Later he followed his own mind in terms of implementing principles that made sense to him. For many years he controlled his stock consisting of cattle, sheep and goats using conventional fencing and a wagon wheel configuration. However, he was always concerned about the fact that he was not getting sufficient herd effect and high enough stock density which he saw as essential to kick start the ecosystem and efficiently utilise the veld. After a visit to my property in Zimbabwe he returned to the arid Karoo fully intent on using electric fences in order to create hundreds of paddocks per herd. This he did in style in accordance with his high standards – portable water troughs designed too keep water clean and gates opening automatically at preset times.

Andre is also one of those individuals who wanted to share his ideas on how to restore the Karoo to its former glory. He went out of his way to involve researchers with his grazing project that was able achieve a stock density of over 1000 Large Stock Units per hectare and a dramatic increase (at least a quadrupling) in stocking rate. It is extremely unfortunate, and an indictment against the academics involved, that they have neither acknowledged nor followed up on Andre's dramatic breakthrough. We can only hope that future generations will see the value in what was achieved on Elandsfontein.

PHOTOS 22.18 and **22.19**: *The scenes above should be posted on billboards around the world as a case study in perseverance and a remarkable breakthrough in natural resource management in an arid environment. Photo 22.18 shows a mixed herd of cattle, sheep and goats moving under an automatically opening gate. Photo 22.19 illustrates the degree of plant (grasses and shrubs) utilisation Andre is able to achieve. This is one of the major reasons he was able to increase stocking rate so drastically. A big problem with conventional management is selective grazing.*

PHOTO 22.20: *Andre, quite rightly, places a lot of emphasis on clean water. This lightweight portable trough designed and built by him allows cattle, sheep and goats to drink clean water without competition from bigger animals. It is clear from the design that animals will drink their fill and move away.*

CARLETONVILLE, SOUTH AFRICA

Jaco Prinsloo is another example of an outsider (insurance business) not knowing what can't be done in terms of ranching. In a very short period of time he was running several thousand cattle under very high stock density on purchased land. The increase in grass utilisation and improved grass vigour resulted in a quadrupling of stocking rate to 1 Large Stock Unit per hectare. What was also noteworthy in Jaco's case was the excellent body condition of cattle due to frequent moves per day onto fresh grazing as well as effective rumen supplementation.

PHOTOS 22.21 *and* ***22.22****: Dramatic photos taken on Jaco Prinsloo's property. Photo 22.20 shows the impact of herds of up to 800 cows concentrated at densities of approximately 3000 cattle per hectare. Jaco actively managed for good body condition as can be gauged from Photo 22.21 showing conventionally bred cows that have grazed non-selectively for a year.*

VENTERSTAD, SOUTH AFRICA

Dirkie Ackerman showed how sheep can be controlled with electric fences and used to create sufficient impact to move the process of succession forward from shrub to grass. It requires effort and single-mindedness to create sufficient impact with sheep to step over the threshold, in terms of herd effect, separating positive change from no change. He was able to do this on a large scale.

PHOTOS 22.23 *and* ***22.24****: The left hand photo illustrates the degree of control and impact possible with sheep by using two energised wires erected and moved by herdsmen. The patches of predominantly grass that can be seen in the photo to the right is where impact was high enough (sufficient stock density to create herd effect; night paddocks) in order to cross the threshold required to move the process of succession forward.*

LADY GREY, SOUTH AFRICA

Marcel van der Merwe is a pioneer in implementing Ultrahigh Density Grazing in rugged and cold mountainous terrain. This environment has unique challenges. Foremost amongst these are extremely steep mountain slopes where physical soil disturbance is undesirable but where stock densities need to be high enough in order to reduce the degree of selective grazing. He overcame this by using these areas as holding areas over weekends by leaving cattle there for two days at a reasonably high stock density ensuring acceptable grass utilisation. Another problem is the cold climate and tick-borne diseases requiring hardier cattle. This is being overcome by the introduction of Africa breed blood in the form of Nguni and Boran (inherently good body condition) into predominantly Bonsmara with some Galloway. This will enable him to achieve a doubling of productivity in line with a doubling of stocking rate.

PHOTOS 22.25 and 22.26: Excellent grass utilisation on mixed veld (left) by Marcel van der Merwe. The ruggedness of the terrain can be gauged by the steep mountain slopes in the background. In order to breed an adapted genotype African breed blood is being introduced as evidenced by the calves pictured on the right.

NANGA SUGAR ESTATE, ZAMBIA

The cattle section of Nanga Sugar Estate near Mazabuka in Zambia is managed by Stanley Hachikuyu whose professionalism and managerial skills epitomise a new level of ranch management in tropical Africa. This man, together with his well trained staff, are paving the way for a potentially revolutionary change from subsistence cattle production to highly productive commercial ranching in this part of the world. Stanley must be commended for his perseverance in controlling cattle with electric fences under difficult conditions. Things have become easier for him now that he is able to use braided steel cable on reels instead of cumbersome 12 gauge high strain wire.

***PHOTOS** 22.27 and **22.28** (Courtesy of Chris Rogers): Stanley Hachikuyu inspecting well utilised and impacted veld grazed during the dry season (left). The photo on the right indicates the required stock density (1000 to 3000 cattle per hectare) in order to utilise the low "octane" grasses found in the seasonally wet tropics.*

MKUSHI, ZAMBIA

Several farmers from Mkushi in north-central Zambia, namely Andrew and Corral Moffat, Raubie and Sally Greyvenstein and Simon and Adrienne Hunt are pioneering the use of Animal Impact in order to utilise, and hopefully decrease, an extremely unpalatable grass (Sporobolus pyramidalis) that has become dominant due to past management. They are using weaned calves and growing them out with extra feed on the worst affected areas. Hopefully the results they are achieving will encourage them to manage all their cattle under a regime of high impact and non-selective grazing.

PHOTOS 22.29 and *22.30* *(Courtesy Chris Rogers): Calves on the property of the Moffat's near Mkushi, Zambia. The degree of control and good body condition is very evident.*

TAMPICO, MEXICO and FLORIDA, USA

Jaime Elizondo Braun, formerly of Tampico in Mexico and now living in Florida, USA is unique in his love for the land and steadfastness in implementing workable solutions. My involvement with him started a few years ago when he contacted me in connection with UltraHigh Density Grazing. His enthusiasm was so high that even before I visited him in Mexico he had already implemented high Animal Impact and Non-Selective Grazing with the use of electric fences on his ranch. We have now teamed up to give ranchers worldwide practical advice on how to improve their land and animals.

PHOTOS 22.31 and *22.32: Cattle grazing pasture (left) and reverting forest (right) on the Elizondo ranches near Tampico in Mexico. A big revelation is the fact that they can now use cattle to control reverting forest in lieu of expensive machinery.*

PHOTOS 22.33 and **22.34**: *The photo on the left shows the dramatic results Jaime is achieving in Florida with high Animal Impact. Note the efficient grass utilisation and even spread of dung. Jaime was also instrumental in introducing the Zimbabwe Mashona breed to Florida. This breed was developed on low "octane" grass in the high altitude tropics and is unique as an efficient convertor of poor quality grass.*

VERCUIEL BOERDERY, SETLOGOLE, SOUTH AFRICA

Cas and Henriette Breedt are a dedicated, young couple who manage the cattle section of Vercuiel Boerdery (Pierre Vercuiel) near Setlagoli in the north-east Kalahari region of South Africa. Cas is responsible for the 2000 plus cow herd and Henriette for the feedlot. Vercuiel Boerdery is one of the pioneers in improved veld management in this semi-arid region using a wagon wheel layout with sub-divisions of the "spoke" created by portable electric cross-fences. Their stocking rate is double the conventionally accepted norm.

Cas has recently initiated a programme of breeding Veldmasters with extremely positive results on the veld and in the feedlot. Although the emphasis in Veldmaster breeding is efficient grass conversion and high practical fertility the results in the feedlot have impressed Henriette – ease of fattening and a very high dressing percentage (high meat: bone ratio).

PHOTOS 22.35 and **22.36**: *The Foundation Veldmaster bull on the left is a Boran/Tuli combination used by Cas on different crossbred cows mainly of Bonsmara/Brahman/European origin. The young bull pictured on the right is one of the progeny. He excelled in terms of grass conversion efficiency with a Yearling Maturity Score in the top 10% (branded **Y–10** on the left shoulder).*

PHOTOS 22.37 and **22.38**: *Pictured on the left is a two-year-old Veldmaster cow and calf. The Standard of Excellence of Veldmasters is determined by 2 + 3 year calving. The photo on the right illustrates the wagon wheel layout with cattle being controlled by a portable electric cross-fence. Pastures are dominated by drought hardy grasses – Cenchrus cilliaris and Anthephora pubescence.*

APPENDIX

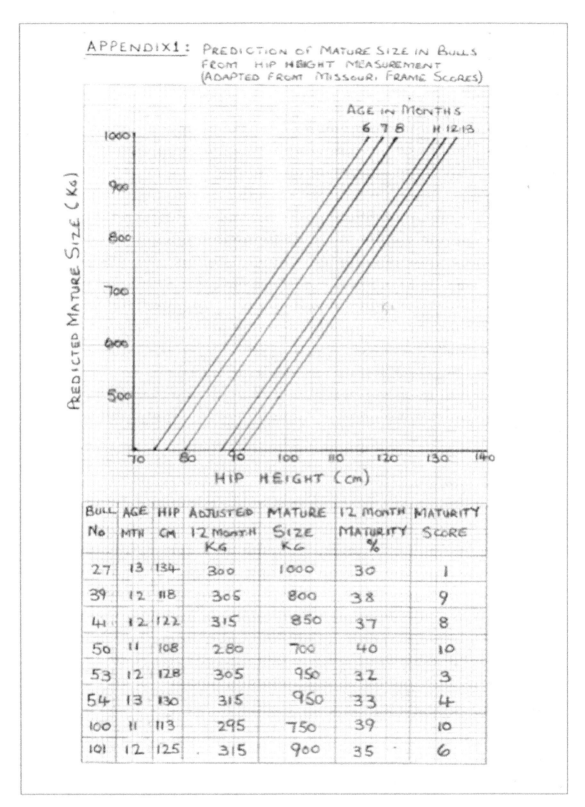

BULL No	AGE MTH	HIP CM	ADJUSTED 12 MONTH KG	MATURE SIZE KG	12 MONTH MATURITY %	MATURITY SCORE
27	13	134	300	1000	30	1
39	12	118	305	800	38	9
41	12	122	315	850	37	8
50	11	108	280	700	40	10
53	12	128	305	950	32	3
54	13	130	315	950	33	4
100	11	113	295	750	39	10
101	12	125	315	900	35	6

APPENDIX 1: PREDICTION OF MATURE SIZE IN BULLS FROM HIP HEIGHT MEASUREMENT (Adapted from Missouri Frame Scores).

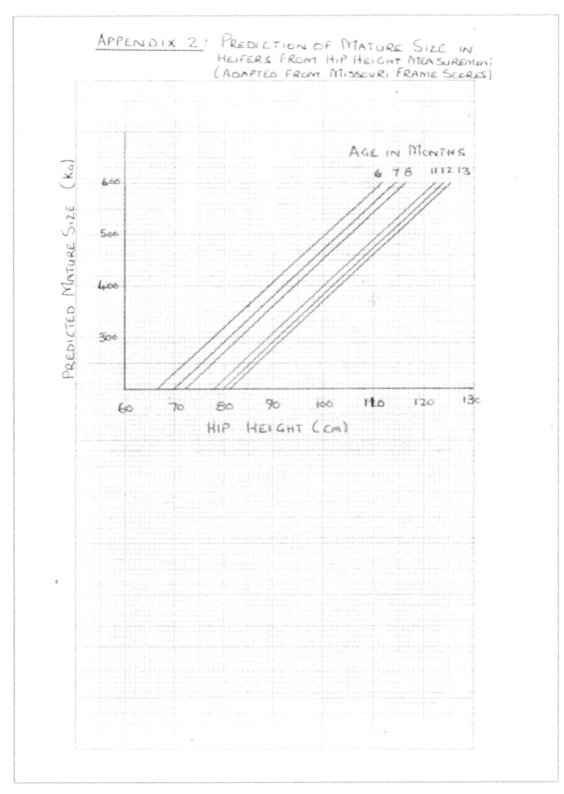

APPENDIX 2: PREDICTION OF MATURE SIZE IN HEIFERS FROM HIP HEIGHT MEASUREMENT (Adapted from Missouri Frame Scores).

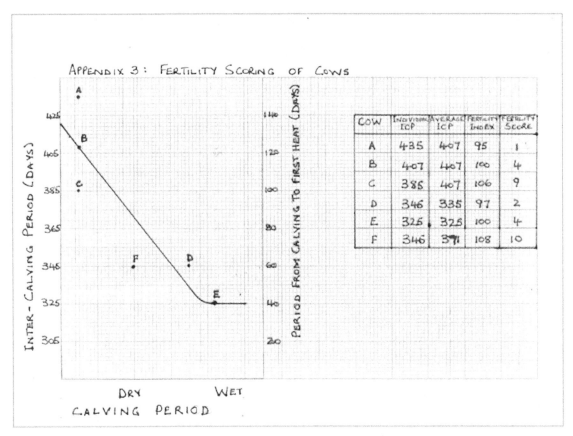

APPENDIX 3: FERTILITY SCORING OF COWS.

GLOSSARY

Absolute Intake: The total intake of feed by an animal

Academic Fertility: Fertility that is determined by inherent hormonal balance and good body condition resulting from artificially improved (selective grazing; energy feed) nutrition

ADG: Average Daily Gain

Animal Impact: The physical impact on soil and plants created by a dense herd

"Bosbul": Roughly translated means mongrel or village bull

BLUP: Best Linear Unbiased Prediction

Carrying capacity: The number of animals that can be supported by the available forage

CD: Cattle Days

Dipping: Chemical control of cattle in order to control ticks

"Draadkar": Equivalent to wiry and slab-sided.

EBV: Estimated Breeding Value

EPD: Expected Progeny Difference

FCE: Feed Conversion Efficiency. Data obtained from South African Phase C feedlot test

Genotype: The genetic composition of an individual

Herd Effect: The careless trampling of a herd of animals

Highveld: High altitude countryside

ICP: Inter-Calving Period - period (days) between two consecutive calving dates

Index: Expression of performance figures with 100 being average

Livestock Unit (LU): See Large Stock Unit (LSU) below.

Large Stock Unit (LSU): A LSU is equivalent to a cow or two suckling calves. A yearling can be considered to be ¾ of an LSU

Lowveld: Low altitude countryside

Maize stover: Corn plant residue left after combining

Moribund grass: Old and grey (oxidising) grass

NSG: Non Selective Grazing

Overgrazing: Repeated grazing of plants before recovery of root energy reserves

Overresting: Prolonged lack of defoliation of plants or non-disturbance of plants and soil

Phase C test: South African cattle performance test where growth (ADG) and feed conversion (FCE) are measured under feedlot conditions

Phase D test: South African cattle performance test where growth (ADG) is measured in the feedlot or on grazing

Phenotype: The appearance or performance of an individual as determined by the combined action of genotype and environment

PPAP: Post Partum Anoestrous Period - period (days) from calving to first oestrous cycle

Relative Intake: An animal's intake relative to its size

Pony-type: In reference to stocky, early maturing cattle, particularly bulls

Practical Fertility: Fertility as determined by inherent hormonal balance **and** inherent body condition (low feeding regime)

SDG: Short Duration Grazing

Sourveld: Low "octane" grazing

Stocking rate: The number of animals on the land

Stock density: The number of animals grazing on one acre or one hectare at any given time

Sweetveld: High "octane" grazing

UHDG: UltraHigh Density Grazing

Veld: Range in the narrow sense and countryside in the broad sense

Veldmaster: Cattle composite containing at least 50% African breed blood and selected for efficiency of grass conversion with productivity measured as *sustainable profit per unit of land*

CONVERSION TABLES

Kilograms (kg) to Pounds (lb): kg x 2.2 = lb

Pounds (lb) to Kilograms (kg): lb / 2.2 = kg

Hectares (ha) to Acres (ac): ha x 2.5 = ac

Acres (ac) to Hectares (ha): ac / 2.5 = ha

Kilometres (km) to Miles (mi): km x 0.6 = mi

Miles (mi) to Kilometres (km): mi / 0.6 = km

Made in the USA
Las Vegas, NV
31 October 2024

10816823R00162